Poetry Explorers

Poems From Scotland

Edited by Helen Davies

First published in Great Britain in 2009 by

 Young**Writers**

Remus House
Coltsfoot Drive
Peterborough
PE2 9JX
Telephone: 01733 890066
Website: www.youngwriters.co.uk

Foreword

At Young Writers our defining aim is to promote an enjoyment of reading and writing amongst children and young adults. By giving aspiring poets the opportunity to see their work in print, their love of the written word as well as confidence in their own abilities has the chance to blossom.

Our latest competition Poetry Explorers was designed to introduce primary school children to the wonders of creative expression. They were given free reign to write on any theme and in any style, thus encouraging them to use and explore a variety of different poetic forms.

We are proud to present the resulting collection of regional anthologies which are an excellent showcase of young writing talent. With such a diverse range of entries received, the selection process was difficult yet very rewarding. From comical rhymes to poignant verses, there is plenty to entertain and inspire within these pages. We hope you agree that this collection bursting with imagination is one to treasure.

Contents

Cramond Primary School, Edinburgh

Dean Park Primary School, Balerno

East Plean Primary School, Plean

Fallin Primary School, Fallin

Ferryhill Primary School, Edinburgh

The Poems

The Magic Box

(Inspired by 'Magic Box' by Kit Wright)

In my magic box . . .
Is the scent of purple lavender
From ancient gardens that only
Fairies can reach,
The river Shiany that I can see the past and future in.

I will put in the box . . .
Dinosaur fossils,
I can make a combination of numbers
That shimmer in the moonlight.

I will trap in my box . . .
A black shadow at the edge of space
That nobody can find.

When I open the box . . .
I hear birds singing in the language Birlay.

My box is bright pink with orange squiggly lines,
It comes from Lancshmeer.

I shall
Ski on a really big ice cream, eat it and
Also bathe in it until I fall asleep.

Rachel McGovern (9)

Abernethy Primary School, Nethy Bridge

The Magic Box

(Inspired by 'The Magic Box' by Kit Wright)

I will put in the box . . .
A shiny silver Star Wars lightsaber,
From the first Jedi to kill a sith,
A chocolate Kinder Egg from the edge of space,
Three golden wishes spoken in Shokariu.

I will put in the box . . .
A feather from an osprey flying
Higher than the clouds,
A thirteenth month and a
Fireball from the sun.

My box is fashioned from . . .
Sapphire-coloured steel with cobra lines
Which slither down my box
And the heads come off it
To stop people stealing it.

Its hinges are made from emeralds and
Diamonds from the end of the world.

I shall battle in the stars, and land
In a river of the clearest water in the world.

Lewis Harkiss (9)
Abernethy Primary School, Nethy Bridge

The Magic Box

(Inspired by 'The Magic Box' by Kit Wright)

I will put in the box . . .
A big, red Chinese dragon's dreams
As he is sleeping,
Mum's homemade banana loaf,
A magic unicorn trotting along in an open field.

I will put in the box . . .
A spiral shell from the Caribbean sea,
The biggest smile in the world,
A little dog playing with a spotty ball,
An eight day week.

My box is fashioned from . . .
Gold with a glass lid
That has little balls on it,
With little fairies flying and chasing each other.

Its hinges are birds' wings that are blue and red.

I shall trot along on a white horse, along a Caribbean beach
And look at the golden sand.

Lisi Smith (9)
Abernethy Primary School, Nethy Bridge

Stars — Haiku

Giant balls of fire
Sparkling brightly in the sky
Wishes all come true.

Nula Langmuir (9)
Abernethy Primary School, Nethy Bridge

3

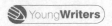
Autumn In The Woods

I feel a chilly nip in the air,
I see the shiny, sparkling dew on the
Silver spiders' webs shimmering like crystals.

Bright red and white toadstools
Like fairy houses hiding in the long, damp grass,
Umbrellas for sleepy voles.

I watch the colourful, dry, curled
Leaves dancing like ballerinas down
To the pine-needled floor.

Misty breath like Jack Frost
Flows out of my mouth,
Squirrels scrambling and scurrying
Searching for scrummy nuts to hide.

Berry feast of blueberries and rosehips,
Ready for the hungry birds.

I feel a chilly nip in the air,
Yes autumn is here.

P5 Class Poem

Abernethy Primary School, Nethy Bridge

Little Hedgehog – Haiku

Hedgehog in the snow,
Curling up with the leaves, warm.
He wakes up, it's spring.

Angus Sandison (9)

Abernethy Primary School, Nethy Bridge

The Blitz

Thundering of bombs,
Firing of rifles,
Noise of passing enemy planes,
Screaming of terrified people.

Smouldering buildings,
Eye-watering smoke,
Rotting bodies lying in the streets,
The musty damp houses.

Fire rising to the sky,
Soldiers marching smartly,
Blood from where murdered humans lay,
Mini craters from the crashing bombs.

Cuts and bruises, in pain,
Freezing cold wind on my cheeks,
Fingers trembling with fear,
Scarred, tired legs plodding on the street.

Rachel Smith & Ellen Grant (11)
Abernethy Primary School, Nethy Bridge

Autumn

A utumn is coming
U nder the bushes animals sleeping
T all trees wave fast in the wind
U mbrellas sheltering us from the rain
M ist in the mornings
N ights get longer.

Julia Smolarz (8)
Abernethy Primary School, Nethy Bridge

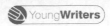

The Blitz

The sky is dark and cloudy,
And the night is sure to be long.
Everyone is waiting, no one can relax,
In the distance lights are moving.
All of a sudden the war is upon us,
Like a storm it rumbles and growls.
The thin beams of light suddenly erupt everywhere.
The high-pitched wailing of the air-raid sirens,
Babies crying, men shouting,
Bodies, fire, destruction.
The crack of guns is getting closer,
I hear my mother yelling, 'Quick to the basement!'
I grab my father's photo and my baby sister,
The basement is cold and a bare bulb is our only light.
The swish of planes, bombs exploding,
Coming nearer and nearer and . . .
Everything goes dark and silent.

Rachel Crane (10)
Abernethy Primary School, Nethy Bridge

Autumn

A utumn is here,
U nder the leaves a hedgehog is sleeping,
T rees whispering to each other,
U mbrellas held high while rain drips,
M ug of cosy, warm hot chocolate,
N ice scone and a cup of tea.

Rowan Langmuir (8)
Abernethy Primary School, Nethy Bridge

The Magic Box

(Inspired by 'Magic Box' by Kit Wright)

I will put in the box . . .
A shiny, sparkling star that has just fallen from the sky,
A fast unicorn from the lovely, flowery meadow,
A spiral shell from the ancient deep sea.

I will put in the box . . .
A curled leaf from the wet rainforest,
A fluffy, black feather from a noisy crow,
A crystal from a corner of a dark cave.

My box is fashioned from . . .
Gold jewels from bumpy stones from the beach,
With silver stars,
The hinges are made from butterflies' wings.

I shall meet a furry bear and ride on him
Through the branchy woods.

Sophie Young (9)
Abernethy Primary School, Nethy Bridge

William

W onky writer,
I am good at rugby,
L ikes hot dogs,
L oves football,
I am awesome,
A bsolutely cool,
M aster of cheese.

William Moncrieff (8)
Abernethy Primary School, Nethy Bridge

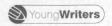

The Magic Box

(Inspired by 'Magic Box' by Kit Wright)

I will put in the box . . .
Finlay choking on a Wotsit,
A minotaur's horn at the bottom of a dinosaur's stomach,
The wail of one of the last dinosaurs as it dies.

I will put in the box . . .
Someone walking to the boiling centre of the Earth,
A pirate raising the Jolly Roger at midnight,
A worm eating all the bananas in the world.

My box is fashioned from the fur of a woolly mammoth,
With patches of gold.
Its hinges are made of ivory and coal from ancient mines.

I shall run away from all the dark, evil things in my box
And curl up in a chair.

Ben Pilkington (9)
Abernethy Primary School, Nethy Bridge

Autumn

I don't like autumn,
Because conkers fall on my head,
And nuts from up above me
And it's sore!
But the only thing
I like about autumn,
Is hot chocolate.

Wayde Buley (7)
Abernethy Primary School, Nethy Bridge

The Magic Box

(Inspired by 'Magic Box' by Kit Wright)

I will put in the box . . .
The skull of a bearded dragon,
A rare animal from the past called Zog,
A minotaur's head from the Palace of Knossos.

I will put in my box . . .
A magical stone from Atlantis,
A giant millipede eating all the apple pies in the world,
A six-headed monster that everyone is running away from.

My box is fashioned from buffalo fur,
With bronze from the past for the inside,
Its hinges are made from gold and silver.

I shall run away from the giant millipede and
Find a nice safe place to curl up in.

Ross Dodds (9)

Abernethy Primary School, Nethy Bridge

Blaine

B laine loves dogs,
L ikes Lego too,
A m good at looking after pets,
I have a wobbly tooth,
N ew baby coming,
E ven cares for beavers.

Blaine Dodds (7)

Abernethy Primary School, Nethy Bridge

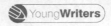

Autumn

It's autumn, time for fun,
Squirrels collecting nuts,
Hedgehogs sleep in the cold wind,
Huddled under leaves,
Mud getting deeper,
Conkers on the ground,
Tall trees becoming more and more bare,
Red, orange and yellow leaves cover the garden,
It's definitely autumn!

Molly Vaughan (7)
Abernethy Primary School, Nethy Bridge

The Moon – Haiku

Yellow plate at night,
Light reflecting from the sun,
Pale face looking down.

Becky Smith (9)
Abernethy Primary School, Nethy Bridge

Stars – Haiku

The sparkly bright stars,
Like diamonds on a curtain,
Shining in vast space.

Alisha Young (9)
Abernethy Primary School, Nethy Bridge

Life Is Fun

I like art,
Shading, chalking,
My hands all messy,
Painting,
Everything.

I like American football,
Throwing, catching, tackling,
But I don't ever let it touch the ground.

I like my PS2,
Games, games, games,
Racing, action, excitement,
Fingers furiously fast, heart
Pounding.

Life is fun.

Callum Amos (9)
Achfary Primary School, Achfary

Washed Up At Shore

As I lay there helplessly, the sun blazes into my eyes,
The salty sea air blows through my hair,
I try and yell for help but the shock makes me breathless
And I feel so weak,
So here I lay, like a dead sea turtle,
Washed up at shore,
Stuck on its back by its own dead weight,
My eyes start to close,
I don't know if I am dead or not,
I feel as if I am trapped,
My brain tells me I am dead,
But my heart tells me I am still alive.

Claire Barnes-Miller (11)
Achfary Primary School, Achfary

What I Like

I like playing on my football table,
It's like a football pitch inside,
With football players stuck onto a metal pole,
I hold the two handles and twist,
I try to get the ball near my team so I can shoot.

I like going fishing with my dad,
Because I have a job I like,
To throw creels out the side of the boat,
Hauling them in
And stacking them on top of each other.

Danny Tebay
Achfary Primary School, Achfary

My Dream School

A chievement is encouraged in everything I do at Auldhouse,
U niform is worn to Auldhouse every day,
L ots of laughter and fun at Auldhouse, I am in a good mood,
D inners at Auldhouse are eaten, healthy and good,
H onest and trust between each and every one at Auldhouse,
O rganised by teachers at Auldhouse who care about everyone,
U nusual sports I get to try, like curling, at Auldhouse,
S afe at all times, no bullies to make me cry,
E xercise is encouraged to keep me fit, lots of running at
Auldhouse, I don't like to sit.

P E and art are subjects I do in primary one,
R ead, read and read, at primary I am encouraged to do,
I nteresting topics and outings at primary in May,
M aths and computing at primary, we do every day,
A chieving our goals whilst having lots of fun in primary one,
R eading and writing we are taught in primary one,
Y ou may know my dream school, as it's
Auldhouse Primary School.

Emily Craig (10)
Auldhouse Primary School, East Kilbride

My Dream School

My dream school would have
Teachers who are very good
And no one who is really rude.

My dream school would also have
Pleasant teachers
And no one who makes fun of people's cultures or features.

In my dream school
Every child would be treated fairly and equally,
Even if their parents helped the school every day.

In my dream school,
Children would be happy and free,
And there would be no teachers that have a look saying,
'You better not mess with me!'

Rachel Keeley (11)
Auldhouse Primary School, East Kilbride

My Dream School

My dream school is where I feel happy,
Where I am treated like all of the other children,
A place where I feel safe,
It is a place where I have fun,
Where I can play,
Where I find new friends,
It is a place where I am encouraged to work harder,
In my dream school, I want to be helpful,
My dream school is the school
I am in right now.

Caitlin Campbell (9)
Auldhouse Primary School, East Kilbride

What Am I?

As an egg my life will begin,
As I sit and wonder what I am in,
Then one day I will break free,
From the egg that I was in at the top of the tree,
Next I will be a caterpillar and eat everything on my way,
So I can grow bigger day by day,
I eat apples, pears and plums,
So I can get fatter, do the sums,
I'm dying to get fatter, please make it soon,
So I can build a beautiful cocoon,
So very soon I will fly in the sky,
And I will be a beautiful butterfly.

Yasmin Sadiq (10)
Bellahouston Primary School, Glasgow

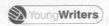

Death

I don't know how
I don't know why
I don't know when
I don't know where.

You will wait in the silence to hear, but nothing.
You will listen, but you will hear nothing.
But still it will come.
I wonder what you are made of
I wonder where you come from
You visit without an appointment.

Oh how I hate you
You took my granny away.
Too little time to do make amends
For things that I've done.
Too little time to do things
I've left unsaid, undone.

With every effort that I make
I know at least I've tried.
Just helping people to wear a smile
Makes me feel like a good girl.

Gugu Nleya (10)
Bellahouston Primary School, Glasgow

Dogs

Dogs are:
So mean to play with,
So dirty to deal with,
Sometimes they are so happy,
Sometimes they are so snappy,
But remember even then . . .
They can be jolly happy.

Nauman Butt (10)
Bellahouston Primary School, Glasgow

Football

I like football,
Manchester United football team,
I like to cheer,
I like to scream,
Because it is my favourite team,
That's why I cheer and scream,
Because it is the most popular sport in the world.

Yusuf Bamba (9)
Bellahouston Primary School, Glasgow

Cars

Fast cars,
Slow cars,
I like all types of cars,
From Hondas to Ferrari,
And motorbikes too,
I like cars, how about you?

Subhaan Rana (11)
Bellahouston Primary School, Glasgow

Shopping

Shopping is bright pink
It tastes like a red juicy strawberry
And it smells like a nice red rose
Shopping looks like a sandy beach
It makes me buy that dress.

Semone Haider (10)
Bellahouston Primary School, Glasgow

My Guinea Pig

A furry creature
A celery muncher
A long sleeper
A bundle of joy.

Katie Morris (10)
Burrelton Primary School, Burrelton

My Dad

My dad
Was very sad
He was very unwell
So when he needed something, he rang a bell
The doctor said he had cancer
And it's a shame because he was a very good dancer
When he was well, he was so much fun
But all that was almost done
The doctor said we could take him home
But one of his eyes went red and really shone
Sooner or later, I knew he was going to die
And when he did, he had to wear his wedding tie
He wrote to us before he passed away
And somehow he knew it was today
Hundreds of people came to say goodbye
And I seem to remember, they all cried
So you see it has been a hard life for me
And when my dad died, I wouldn't eat my tea
So I wrote this poem to go in this book
And I hope you have a wee look.

Eilidh Adamson (11)
Burrelton Primary School, Burrelton

Friends!

A friend is like a cherry,
On top of a strawberry bun,
A friend is like a flower,
That dances beneath the sun.

Morgan Mauchline (11)
Burrelton Primary School, Burrelton

A' Aboot Ma Family

First there's ma maw who's awful grumpy,
But when I'm oot the room, she is quite happy,
Next it's ma da, he's ma best friend,
He really likes tractors, they're his new trend.

O' then there's Catie,
There's nae way she's a lady,
She can really mak me angry,
She would mak a better laddie.

Watch out, here comes Danny,
He's ma silly little manny,
Now there's Munchys in her bed,
Dreamin' she could scratch wee Danny's head.

Now ma granny's a different story,
I love 'er sae much I'd gie 'er a trophy,
All o' them are such treasures,
Havin' them as ma family's a pleasure.

Rianne Nairn (11)
Burrelton Primary School, Burrelton

My Teacher

My teacher is an exploding volcano,
My teacher is the wicked witch of the west,
My teacher is a hungry lion ready to pounce,
My teacher is a furious monster,
My teacher is a deadly viper,
My teacher is well, angry at me.

Bronagh Pennycook (12)
Burrelton Primary School, Burrelton

The Bestest Friends Ever!

No one could ever come between me and my girls,
They're as precious as a string of pearls,
All of them have the kindest souls,
When we're at a party, we get out of control,
They're the most inspiring people in my life,
They're so gorgeous, never any trouble or strife,
I'll always hold them close to my heart,
They know we'll never be miles apart,
All of them know I'm stupid,
They could be the brand new cupid,
They'll be what they want to be,
Not what any boys want to see,
If anyone makes me cry, they'll give them a *POW*,
Sorry, but I've got to go now.

Amy Garthwaite (11)
Burrelton Primary School, Burrelton

Swimming

Dive in
Six lengths
Goggles, nose pegs
Splishing, splashing
Speedy flippers
Backstroke, breaststroke
Front crawl, butterfly
Relay races.

Get soaked!

Holly Kinmont (10)
Burrelton Primary School, Burrelton

21

Race

The wind blowing through my hair,
This feeling is very rare,
Short breathing, heart pounding, legs pumping,
Now it's time for some long jumping,
People running past me now,
The sideline cat squeals, 'Miaow!'
Attention goes, I fall and trip,
I'll live, it's just a cut lip,
Everyone is screaming my name,
I will not hang my head in shame,
Once again I finished last,
But oh well, I had a laugh,
These are the best things in a race,
Just remember to tie your lace!

Ross Whamond (11)
Burrelton Primary School, Burrelton

My Molly Moo

Mayhem-maker
Puzzle-solver
Sweetie-eater
TV-watcher
Cutie-pie
Throws-tantrums
Bunny-hugger
Bossy-boots
When she smiles, she always gets her way.

Abbey Hutchison (10)
Burrelton Primary School, Burrelton

All About School!

School can be good,
If I'm in the mood,
When we do drama,
We have to act like a llama,
I like gym,
But once I hurt my limb,
Oh reading, how I dread,
I'd rather be in my bed,
Spelling is great,
With letters of eight,
Maths is fun,
When you measure a bun.

Max Avolio (10)
Burrelton Primary School, Burrelton

Donkey

Funny sounds,
Swishing tail,
Gentle touch,
Fun rider,
Grass eater,
Quiet creature,
Soft coat,
Trotting hooves,
My granny's favourite.

Caitlin Nairn (10)
Burrelton Primary School, Burrelton

Alien!

Green skin
Human abductor
Three-eyes
Large fingers
UFO operator
Weird body
Human-eater
Spindly antennae
A hideous monster.

Natalie Payne (11)
Burrelton Primary School, Burrelton

Scotland

Ben Nevis and bad weather
Loch Ness will live forever
Irn-Bru is our drink
The battle of Bannock Burn makes you think
Robbie Burns was an amazing poet
And you and me both know it
Us in Scotland are oh so brave
We'll be fighting until we're in our gave
Scotland the brave!

Ryan McGregor (11)
Burrelton Primary School, Burrelton

My Cat

Fierce-fighter
Perfect purr
Super-scratcher
Hound-hater
Sparrow-spier
Softly soft
Cuddle cute
Amazing ability
My feline friend.

Emma Croal (12)
Burrelton Primary School, Burrelton

Bubblegum

Bubblegum, bubblegum,
Chewable, lots of fun,
Big balloons, sticky faces,
Bubblegum, bubblegum.

Bubblegum, bubblegum,
Multicolour, different taste,
Never let it go to waste,
Bubblegum, bubblegum.

Christie Whittle (10)
Burrelton Primary School, Burrelton

Football

I have to play football now,
But wait, it's been cancelled, how?
I think to myself, *what can I do?*
When all of a sudden, I hear a cow moo,
I could go for a walk,
Or phone up a friend and talk,
What's the use? It's just not the same,
I miss football and people shouting my name.

Corey Magdziarz (12)
Burrelton Primary School, Burrelton

Dancing

Dancing is like a dream,
The music is loud,
If flows smoothly like a stream,
When I dance I feel proud.

Dancing is fun,
Also hard,
And your hair must be worn in a bun,
When you fall you always get a get well card.

I love to dance,
I know
Ballet comes from France,
It cheers you up when you're low.

Iona Stevenson (10)
Cleish Primary School, Cleish

My Best Friends

All of my friends mean the world to me,
They are all people I couldn't be,
Some like riding, sport and fashion,
Not all my favourite passions.
Lauren likes ponies, plus she's great fun,
And our friendship's never done,
Megan has made up amazing words,
Like 'Hoodes Moodes,' 'Candanas and Sturds'.
Hannah is a tomboy, funky and cool,
She loves sport, did I mention she rules?
Ailsa Brown, what can I say?
She's the same as me in every way.

Iona is great at cross country,
What a great person she is to me,
Eliza likes her horse riding,
She goes to the stables called 'Tiding'.
To me Beth is really tall,
Never have I seen her really small,
I love Shona so much,
Shona Bear, she loves to clutch,
Mia is a funky girl,
She goes to dancing, where she learns to twirl,
Samantha is great at swimming,
Every competition she is winning,
All of my friends, different things they do,
I know that I respect them and it's true!

Ailsa Wilkie (10)
Cleish Primary School, Cleish

Loch Leven

In the middle of the Loch Leven
The water was not even,
Because sixteen years ago
A ship had twenty tons of cargo.

They went across the sea
While the sailors had their tea,
The weather was mild
And the sea was wild.

And that night
There was a light,
It was still in the sky,
And shining in someone's eye.

It was too soon
It couldn't be the moon!
Then the rocks crumbled
And then they tumbled.

They rolled in the mud
And then there was a silent thud,
And when the cargo was set free
It landed at the bottom of the sea.

Callum Buchanan (8)
Cleish Primary School, Cleish

My Time Travel Machine

I have a time travel machine,
And I keep it very clean,
Whenever I go out,
It makes some people shout.

Sometimes I think it will disappear,
But it can reappear,
Whenever it gets out of sight,
It puts on its little light.

Its colour is bright, bright blue,
It comes to show what it can do,
Sometimes it makes me mad,
But it never makes me sad.

Whenever I turn it on,
It sometimes goes wrong,
Goodbye, goodbye, we have to leave,
Oh no, we are going to crash into some trees!

Shona Wilkie (8)
Cleish Primary School, Cleish

My First Prey

Looking for my first prey,
Hunting for a big, scary mammoth,
Carrying my sharp spear,
Quietly creeping behind the mammoth,
Aiming with my eyes and arms,
Caught at last!

Rhona Brown (7)
Cleish Primary School, Cleish

Jacob

Jacob is very cool,
Even when he goes to school.
Jacob is a pro at almost everything,
I like Jacob very much, even when he sings.

He is a very fast runner and beats me in every race,
He likes drawing and can trace.
I like him because he is strong and fit,
He has a special chair in which only he can sit.

Jacob is 8 years old,
He is very strong and bold.
He is my best friend even when he's mean,
Jacob is very funny and will always be on my team.

Ryan Brown (9)
Cleish Primary School, Cleish

Kennings Poem

Name-caller
Big-boaster
Toy-stealer
Copycat
Evil devil
Excuse-maker
Cute face
Great friend
Worst foe,

A brother.

Felix Principe Gillespie (11)
Cleish Primary School, Cleish

Cross Country

C rossing the line as we go
R unning very fast
O ut of breath
S tomaches ache for all the race
S leeping is just a dream.

C ome on, come on, we need to run
O ver hills and far away
U nder the tunnels we go, waiting for the final blow
N ever stop
T ry to run as fast as I can
R ushing to the finishing line
Y ou're finished.

Lewis Caulfield (9)
Cleish Primary School, Cleish

Eliza Bear

Eliza Bear is light brown,
Her lucky number is two,
And her best colour is blue,
She loves being a bear and
She used to have a tear.
She loves the light,
So I hug her tight,
She hates the dark,
But she can't bark,
Eliza Bear is a dude
And is also very good.

Eliza Stevenson (8)
Cleish Primary School, Cleish

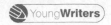

Time Travel

T oday I think I will go to London, it's 1953,
I might go to another planet, but maybe not,
M aybe I'll go to Mars . . . but I like my original idea,
E very time I go I pick up a new source of energy.

T o power up my engine to race across the sky,
R eally, really fast, I love it,
A t the end of the day, I sigh and smile happily,
V arious things happen to my machine,
E very time I get more energy, it keeps expanding,
L ots of space, all for me!

Ailsa Brown (9)

Cleish Primary School, Cleish

Kennings Poem

Food-scoffer
Poop-leaver
Finger-biter
Clothes-chewer
Noise-maker
Cute face
Small, cuddly
Button nose
Little tail
Lovely animal.

Fraser Gosse (11)

Cleish Primary School, Cleish

Rosie Bear

R osie is my favourite toy,
O bviously she is very cute and cuddly,
S hona Bear is her friend,
I love her so much,
E ven when I'm sad, she cheers me up.

B ecause she is my buttercup bear,
E very day she makes me smile,
A friend forever I will have,
R osie is the best!

Mia Archibald (9)
Cleish Primary School, Cleish

Gargoyles

G argoyles sit on a window sill,
A bout to make a jump for a human,
R eaching out for a finger,
G ot it,
O ften he would just rip the skin off,
Y oung gargoyles are much more frightening,
L ights flash in the dark showing the moves of every gargoyle,
E ating time is important,
S mells of blood come through the gutters and through the window.

Hannah Peedle (9)
Cleish Primary School, Cleish

Shark

Big killer
Eats anything
Dangerous devil
Kills humans
Big jaws
So dangerous
Really big
Fish lover
Creature of the deep.

Matthew Gilmour (11)
Cleish Primary School, Cleish

My Island

Cliffs with deep caves,
Sea sparkling in the sun.
White hills with glittering snow,
Nature all around me.
Visitors going to and fro,
Farmers planting golden corn.
Palm trees covering up the sun,
My dream island.

Hector Principe Gillespie (8)
Cleish Primary School, Cleish

The Jungle

The jungle is so creepy,
It is so hot and so steamy,
When you enter the great, big jungle,
All the bugs start to scramble,
When the leaves start to wither,
The mighty tree snake starts to slither,
When the toucans come out at night,
The mighty jaguar's eyes shine bright.

Steven Pollock (10)
Cleish Primary School, Cleish

Football

F ootball crazy, football mad,
O wn goals are very bad,
O ut of the pitch means a corner or a throw in,
T old you I could score a goal,
B anging in the net,
A ll the crowd are very wild,
L ook what skill he has,
L ook, he'll be the one to score the winning goal!

Daniel Munro (9)
Cleish Primary School, Cleish

Monsters

M ighty looking eyes,
O dd little face,
N obody likes them,
S cary as can be,
T errible sharp claws,
E veryone's scared of them,
R azor-sharp teeth,
S harp teeth can rip your arm off.

Daniel Black (10)
Cleish Primary School, Cleish

Blitz

Sound,
Planes creeping,
Death, pain sneaking,
Bombs spiralling, crashing earthwards,
People run underground,
Sirens screaming,
Everlasting.

Callum Gosse (11)
Cleish Primary School, Cleish

Rugby

It flew straight and true,
I leapt and lost my shoe,
But I still got the ball and passed it through,
With Jimmy Jones on my left,
And Sparky Sprite on my right,
We crashed forward with a thud,
As the players fell in the mud.

Adam Dalgleish (10)
Cleish Primary School, Cleish

Blitz

Blitz,
Enveloping blackout,
Terrifying sirens wailing,
Searchlights scanning the darkened sky,
Huge bombs descending,
Piercing screams,
Death.

Edward Wood (11)
Cleish Primary School, Cleish

Blitzkrieg

Silence,
Complete darkness,
A soft whisper
Of an incoming bomber,
Searchlights shine bright,
Ear piercing screams,
Destruction.

Fred Culley (11)
Cleish Primary School, Cleish

Blitzkrieg

Hitler,
U-boats invade,
The Spitfire's attack,
The siren cries mournfully,
The bombers approach,
Death awaits,
Silence . . .

Christopher Austin (10)
Cleish Primary School, Cleish

Blitzkrieg!

Terror,
People screaming,
The bombers approach,
A quiet hum of the German fleet,
Our death awaits,
Save us!
Silence.

Colum Stevenson (12)
Cleish Primary School, Cleish

Kennings Poem

Hoppity-hop
Giant chizzlers
Long listeners
Soft and silky,
Sweet and small,
Cuddly fur,
Stuffed with love.

Samantha Caulfield (11)
Cleish Primary School, Cleish

My Island

Glistening grass and golden sand,
Deep, dark forest and cool rock pools,
Long, windy roads and trees blowing in the wind,
Jagged mountains with snow on top,
Beautiful butterflies flying in the sky,
My island.

Jenna Jaap (7)
Cleish Primary School, Cleish

WWII – Cinquain

Spitfire.
Death is coming,
Bombs killing innocent,
Destruction in the city, death,
Silence.

Ian Buchanan (11)
Cleish Primary School, Cleish

My Island

Glistening rock pools in the summer sun,
Cold, wet grass in winter,
Golden sand on the shore,
Visitors sailing in their boats,
My island.

Rebecca Peedle (7)
Cleish Primary School, Cleish

Time Travel

T ime machine,
I magine the future,
M emories of the past,
E xtinct dinosaurs from the past.

T he Stone Age,
R emember the past,
A long time ago,
V oices from the present,
E volution,
L ifting hover cars in the future!

Tom McTeir (11)
Cramond Primary School, Edinburgh

In The Past

I nventions that changed the world,
N ew discoveries found all the time,

T rip back in time,
H ouses made out of wood,
E xtreme war carried out,

P roducts developed and made,
A chieving the impossible,
S eeing Elvis Presley,
T rip back in time.

Daniel Bain (12)
Cramond Primary School, Edinburgh

Dolphins

Soothing chirps,
Head bobbing,
Magical jumps,
Soft splashes,
Fast swimmers,
Glowing eyes,
Friendly smiles,
Human lovers,
Intelligent minds.

Sophie Stein (11)
Cramond Primary School, Edinburgh

Polar Bears

Fierce roars,
Cute cuddles,
Fluffy white,
Adoring mothers,
Fish-eaters,
Funny-fighters,
Penguin-chasers,
Attention-seekers,
Human-eaters!

Isla McIlwrick (11)
Cramond Primary School, Edinburgh

Antiquity

A stonished by travellers through time,
N eurotic about where we have been,
T ime moving slowly backwards,
I ndecipherable hieroglyphics,
Q uestioning history,
U ncivilised creatures,
I ndescrible world,
T ired from travelling,
Y elling for help.

Sarah Ghavabesh (11)
Cramond Primary School, Edinburgh

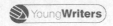

Dragon

Dragon,
Dark scales,
Fierce, fire, smoke,
Hungry, angry, flashing eyes,
Yellow teeth, red
Flying wings
Flight.

Ross McCann (11)

Cramond Primary School, Edinburgh

Bubbly Bunnies

Candyfloss lambs prance through the
Fresh, lush grass while
Fluffy bunnies crunch on
Delicious, juicy carrots,
Soft trickling of a spring stream,
Fills the cool,
New air.

Coreen Grant (11)

Cramond Primary School, Edinburgh

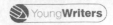

Spring

The new spring sun glistens over me,
Whilst a slight breeze chills my arms,
There are children running and playing
On top of the silvery climbing frame,
But I lie in the grass and look at the new
Buds beginning to grow!

Christopher Pringle (11)
Cramond Primary School, Edinburgh

The Flying Snail

A snail thought he could fly,
But he couldn't because of his eye,
So he stole an eye from a dog,
Who had left it on a log,
And flew for the rest of his life,
Until he found his dream wife.

Patrick David Collings (11)
Cramond Primary School, Edinburgh

The Jungle — Cinquain

Frogs burp,
Blasting colours,
Monkeys eat bananas,
Hear water gushing everywhere,
Snakes hiss.

Charlie Shiel (11)
Cramond Primary School, Edinburgh

The Jungle

Pure green,
Dark and scary,
Tigers roar far away,
Tall, green trees blowing in the breeze.
You're trapped!

Megan Gaskin (11)
Cramond Primary School, Edinburgh

The Jungle — Cinquain

Snakes hiss,
Gigantic trees,
Monkeys swing from the trees,
Tigers roar with ferocity,
Jungle.

Ewen Cullen (11)
Cramond Primary School, Edinburgh

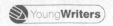

Monkeys – Cinquain

Cute face,
Howling so loud,
Swinging from the branches,
Munching bananas all day long,
Naughty.

Beth Warren (11)

Cramond Primary School, Edinburgh

Happiness – Haiku

So happy am I,
So great I could touch the sky,
I'm jumping with joy!

Lucie Scrimgeour (11)

Cramond Primary School, Edinburgh

Rugby – Haiku

Oh rugby is mad,
Hair flying and feet kicking,
It is a mad sport!

Harry Irvine (11)

Cramond Primary School, Edinburgh

If The Earth . . .

If the Earth were only two metres away,
Floating on top of a building,
People from all over the world would come and gaze at its beauty,
Looking down you could see the stunning oceans,
With fish, whales and dolphins swimming past,
Aeroplanes flying so high you can see them leaving vapour,
Across the sky as they pass,
You could see giraffes, buffaloes and lions,
Running across the deserts in warm Africa,
You could see the Amazon running through the rainforest,
And deserts going for miles and miles,
You could see the polar bears and penguins,
And ice for them to rest on,
If only the Earth was two metres away.

Kirsty Swinton (10)
Dean Park Primary School, Balerno

If The Earth . . .

If the Earth was in front of me,
I would look at the wonderful animals
And I would look at the way the animals move,
I would look at the wonderful waterfalls and
The beautiful mountains,
And the cities and the way they work,
I would look at the North and South Pole,
I would watch the penguins move around the South Pole
And I would feel great.

Jamie Taylor (10)
Dean Park Primary School, Balerno

If The Earth . . .

Winner

If the Earth was a floating ball in a field,
Then this is what it might be like,
People would go goggle-eyed
When they saw the beauty of the rainforest and
The animals living there,
But they would despise the people chopping it down,
They would marvel at the desert and the ever-changing dunes,
But when they screwed up their eyes, they'd see black bits
Where oil was being dug up.
They would marvel at the cities with their vast population,
And cars and planes.
But when they tried to get a closer look,
They would start choking on the gases.
They would think the sea was wonderful with its
Sparkling blue water, hovering waves, whales and colourful fish,
But they would be confused by the ships dropping oil
And blackening the sea.
As they looked across the sea, they would notice the Barrier Reef,
With the unique fish swimming around it,
But as they looked along it,
They would see the bits where pollution was eating at it.
They would look across the African plains with its buffalo and lions,
Picking off just enough to survive.
But then they might see a whole herd dead and people
With guns running off.
They would look at the North and South Pole with
The penguins and the polar bears,
But they would be horrified when they saw the ice melting,
They would look at the hills and the forests,
With the animals climbing around and the birds singing,
But they would feel disappointed when they saw the roads
With cars on them,
They would look at the Ozone in the atmosphere,
With its clouds whispering about and its beautiful rainbows,
They would see the meteors burning,
But also the gases polluting it.

They would see the mountains towering above the clouds,
But then they would see miners hacking massive holes in them,
They would still protect it against everything they could,
But would always worry about the little people destroying
It from the inside out.

Mark McArthur (10)
Dean Park Primary School, Balerno

If The Earth . . .

If the Earth were only a few feet in diameter,
suspended in thin air,
you would notice thousands of beautiful things,
like Niagara Falls and clouds and rivers and oceans.
People would come from far and wide to marvel at
its stunning features,
with indescribable natural wonders such as Victoria Falls
and The Great Wall of China,
and the coral reef where thousands of fish hide in the
holes and tunnels.
People would marvel at the great modern wonders
with cities and roads and buildings,
people would also wonder how things like the Monumental Axis
and the canals,
and the part of Dubai that used to be ocean, but now is land,
could be possible.
People would gaze into the oceans at fish, dolphins,
sharks, great whales and crabs and lobsters, wondering about them.
They would dare not go near it or touch it and would
guard it with their lives, for it was all they had.
If the Earth were only a few feet in diameter.

Oscar Webber (10)
Dean Park Primary School, Balerno

If The Earth . . .

If we could look at the Earth as it is,
We would wonder at the seas and gasp at
The amazing wildlife inside them.
People would be astonished at the way
The monkeys swing from treetop to treetop,
Making their way above a vast green sea,
And if we leaned very close, we could hear the birds
Of many colours, singing and the deep murmur of traffic,
We would worry about the clouds of poison coming out of the cars,
We would wonder and marvel at the marvellous ribbon-like
Rivers coming to the sea, full of a big variety of fish,
People would look in admiration at the snow-topped mountains,
The big birds of prey, circling and ruling the skies,
Wildebeest roaming the plains of Africa and
The mountains of ice floating in the Arctic seas,
We would gasp in horror at the bits of rubbish in the seas,
The black clouds of poison mingling in with the clouds of water,
And the mountains of rubbish hidden underground,
People would want to protect the Earth as a ball,
To stare at it in awe, to gain knowledge from it,
We would be angry with the ant-like people for ruining the globe
And we would want to stop it.

Carla Shearer (10)

Dean Park Primary School, Balerno

If The Earth . . .

If the Earth was only a few feet in diameter,
I'd look at it like the crown jewels,
I'd look at Egypt's giant pyramids and Brazil's lovely forests,
But I'd think what's that?
If I saw a man cut down a tree,
I'd see whales, fish and ships in the blue ocean,
But I'd see people dumping their rubbish and I'd wonder, why?
I'd see the millions of satellites and planes,
But I'd see the planes poisoning the atmosphere,
I'd see Ferraris and Lamborghinis racing round tracks at high speed,
But black gases coming out,
I'd look at the Great Wall of China and the rivers flowing round rocks,
But I'd see litter that had been thrown on the ground,
I'd look at cities, cars, Arctic, Antarctica
And then look at the thin layer of gas called the atmosphere,
I'd see that it was damaged,
I'd wonder why those tiny people weren't looking after their world,
I'd think they're just killing it,
Don't they know how precious it is?
I'd think,
If only the world was a few feet in diameter.

Ben Gourlay (10)
Dean Park Primary School, Balerno

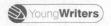

If The Earth . . .

If the Earth were only a few feet in diameter,
floating in space like me,
I would see a little dotted line,
it would be The Great Wall of China.
The climate change would be destroying the Antarctic, ice melting,
polar bears would have nowhere to go,
living in water as it sails across the Arctic Ocean,
the green land disappearing, with the Earth turning round.
Then I could see the pollution building up,
the clouds floating, unfolding, the aeroplanes
pumping out poisonous gases,
red, orange, green lights flashing.
I'd look down, cars starting their engines,
floating out with carbon dioxide into our atmosphere.
The ships would be destroying the coral, going from blue to black.
If our world wasn't polluted, I would be able to see the
cities and the rainforests, gushing blue water from Niagara Falls,
last but not least, animals plodding from one place to another.
Make this valuable world magnificent,
make this *happen!*

Beth Forsyth (10)

Dean Park Primary School, Balerno

If The Earth . . .

If the Earth were only a few metres in diameter
And I was the Creator,
I would look down on it as if it were a precious jewel,
But I would be sad seeing all the gases coming up to me,
I would see the unusual cities full of life and
With massive skyscrapers,
I would be happy seeing monkeys swinging from tree to tree,
Buffalo running across the plains with lions picking a few off
And seeing turquoise blue water filled with fish
And a few whales singing to communicate.
I would be furious looking through the hole in the atmosphere,
At polar bears struggling to get across the ice sheets,
And cars jammed up on one piece of tarmac,
It would be swivelling around with some bits getting
Lighter and other bits darker,
Then all the grey, puffy clouds would cover it forever,
I would be unhappy at the little ant-like
people for doing this.

Murray Baxter (10)
Dean Park Primary School, Balerno

If The Earth . . .

If the Earth was right in front of you,
What would you look at?
I would look at all the fragile little people
And all the precious little animals on land
And in the big, blue oceans,
After that I would try to spot a big, blue whale,
Swimming happily in the sea,
Then I would search for the coral reef with all the fish playing around,
Then I would stare at all the cars moving freely and
The rest of them stuck in traffic,
Afterwards I would look through the clouds at the aeroplanes,
Finally I would look at Africa,
The rainforests and the North and South Pole,
I would see all the penguins and the polar bears
Roaming around freely,
If the Earth was in front of you,
What would you look at?

Catrin Markx (10)

Dean Park Primary School, Balerno

If The Earth . . .

If you could see the Earth in front of you spinning,
Showing you its astonishing snow and ice on the North Pole,
And you can see the polar bears running on the ice looking for food,
You can see the magnificent skyscrapers in the big cities
And thousands of people flooding around them,
You go round the other side and see thousands of beautiful
animals in South Africa.
The streams and rivers gushing through the Amazon
With monkeys swinging from branch to branch,
You could see the aeroplanes fly across the world,
Pumping carbon dioxide in the air,
If you looked very closely, you could see the spectacular
deserts and sand being blown away from the sand dunes,
So if you saw this wonderful world,
Would you still carry on making carbon dioxide
and poisonous fumes?

Evan Kennedy (10)

Dean Park Primary School, Balerno

If The Earth . . .

If the Earth was just in front of me
And just a few feet beneath than me,
I would definitely look down on it,
Firstly I would be astonished how many cars
Are on the city bypasses,
And maybe if I were lucky I would see
A couple of Lamborghinis and maybe a few Ferraris,
But definitely I would have to look down on all the aeroplanes,
Plus I would love to see Niagara Falls and
Seeing a tiny boat going under all the waves,
But most of all, I would love to see all the football pitches,
Especially Old Trafford
And that's what I would like to see.

Scott Macnaughton (10)
Dean Park Primary School, Balerno

If The Earth . . .

From up here, I can see the Great Wall of China
And the green oceans and the Sahara desert with all the camels,
Also I can see the dazzling lights of the cities gleaming up at me.
I can see the polar bears in the North Pole
And the penguins in the South Pole.
It is astonishing when I see the Amazon rainforest
With all the trees and monkeys.
I can see clouds flowing everywhere,
I see the whales, I see the ships sailing,
I can see the Earth.

Stephanie Thomson (10)
Dean Park Primary School, Balerno

If The Earth...

If the Earth were only a few feet in diameter,
Floating a few feet above a field somewhere,
Everybody would come to see it,
You would see penguins, polar bears and seals
Floating in the sea in the North Pole,
Tiger cubs newly born in Africa, all snug and cosy,
Clouds floating across the sky, rainbows arched across the sky,
The sunny hot deserts where no rain falls for months,
Monkeys swinging from tree to tree in Asia,
Children playing in the streets and cars slowly passing by,
All the ships sailing by and the sailors shouting 'Ahoy!'
That's what I would love to see!

Rhea Garrad

Dean Park Primary School, Balerno

If The Earth...

If I could look down on the world,
I'd marvel at the floods of wildlife,
The Amazon with its camouflaged lizards
And its multicoloured birds,
The highlands of Scotland with their deer
And cattle and mountains, lots of mountains.
The massive Pacific with creatures from big blue whales
To the tiniest bit of plankton,
The North Pole with polar bears and great icebergs,
To think that the most powerful creature on Earth,
The human, could destroy all this.

Noah Simpson (10)

Dean Park Primary School, Balerno

Yes Poem!

Yes is a red word,
It's as red as the Devil,
As red as a rose,
As red as the blood
That flows in my veins.
Yes is as red as the sun,
That beats down on me.
Yes is good,
It's sometimes bad,
But when I use it,
It's always *bad!*

Struan Loughlin (10)
Dean Park Primary School, Balerno

Bannockburn

B ones breaking
A rrows shooting
N o rest in fighting
N o horses getting spared
O ften screaming
C lashing swords
K nives slashing
B odies flying in the air
U nderestimating
R acing animals
N o survivors.

Conor Thomson (9)
East Plean Primary School, Plean

The Rat

Sewer lover
Smelly thing
Small, thin
Long tail
Home pet
Cheese lover
Cat enemy
Big whiskers
Small ears
Not grey.

William Millar (9)

East Plean Primary School, Plean

Stirling

S creaming and shouting,
T hundering hooves across the field,
I n the air, bodies flying, groaning,
R aging and rapidly shooting arrows all around,
L ying in agony with blood spurting out,
I n the cave we thank that spider for helping Bruce not to give up,
N ever shall we stand under the English rules between
G ood and evil. Bruce took the crown and Scotland is free!

Lauren Clark (9)

East Plean Primary School, Plean

Stirling

S words flying through the air
T rotting horses everywhere
I n the air, the sound of shooting arrows
R ound and round everywhere
L oudly crashing
I n danger
N o worry, we are
G oing to win!

Matthew McLeod (9)

East Plean Primary School, Plean

Wallace

W onderful, brave and charming
A strong, brave soldier
L eading the Scots to battle
L oud shouting at the enemy
A rrows whistling over your head
C hanting 'Freedom!'
E nemy - back to England!

Nicole Norrie (9)

East Plean Primary School, Plean

Wallace

W illiam Wallace loved to fight,
A nd if he really wanted, he could fight all night,
L oud thundering of hooves,
L ightning, clash, clash!
A lso swords clashing,
C hopping the legs off people,
E nding in a terrible death.

Lyndsay Adamson (9)
East Plean Primary School, Plean

Bruce

B ones breaking
R ed blood spurting
U p on the ground
C harging horses
E asily scared.

Ryan Inglis (9)
East Plean Primary School, Plean

Sword

S tirling is where the battle began,
W ielding the sharp steel in anger,
O n his black steed,
R ight over the shield of the unarmed man,
D ashing backwards to safety.

Kerrie Allan (9)
East Plean Primary School, Plean

Alien Encounters

One day I saw a UFO in the sky,
I said to myself,
Oh my, oh my!
Suddenly it came towards me,
It ended up in the tree,
Then I saw a green light,
It gave me an awful fright!
Then this wee guy came out for a couple of seconds,
It stumbled about then it did a wee dance,
By this time, I needed new pants,
Then I went back in by falling in the wheelie bin,
Then it went back into space,
Away from the human race,
Now that's the end,
Hopefully it won't come back again!

Jordon McColl (10)
Fallin Primary School, Fallin

In Memory Of . . .

Poor John, the Manager
The manager John has actually gone,
Because his colleague sang a song.
It was so dreadful, people shouted,
'Kill, kill, kill!'
Poor John, just because of a crazy song!

In Memory of Mr Seer
In memory of Mr Seer,
He died from drinking beer,
The beer was extremely dear,
They were not at all sad,
Everyone went mad,
Because they were happy,
That the drunk dad had
Gone!

Maisie!
Maisie was football crazy,
She kicked the ball,
She started to tumble and fall,
That's the end of Maisie Trooty,
She'll really miss her footy.

Beth Wilson (10)
Fallin Primary School, Fallin

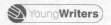

Animals

Animals are great,
There are lots of different kinds of animals,
From furry to slimy and sticky.
Some are born in eggs, some are not,
Some are big and some are small,
Some live in trees, some don't,
Some live in houses.
All animals are great,
We like them and they like us.

Amie Mackie (9)
Fallin Primary School, Fallin

Days Of The Week!

Monday has maths, language and that,
Tuesday has gym and doing fun things,
Wednesday brings joy, no maths at all,
Thursday has playtime, fun once again,
Friday is fun, not much to do,
School's nearly finished, what shall we do?
Saturday comes at last, sleeping not too fast,
Sunday is the last day of the weekend,
Tomorrow is school, starting all over again.

Lauren Catterall (10)
Fallin Primary School, Fallin

My Mum

My mum is very special,
In each and every way,
She helps me with my homework,
Each and every day,
If I didn't have her,
I don't know what I would do,
I'd probably end up in the zoo!

Stuart Boyle (10)
Fallin Primary School, Fallin

Birds

Birds are frilly, birds are feathery,
Some birds are very, very silly,
Some fly, some walk,
But one thing about all birds, they can't talk,
Some birds are colourful,
Some birds make a funny sound,
And all birds drop things on the ground.

Arron Sweeney (10)
Fallin Primary School, Fallin

Old Gone John

Old gone John liked to eat plums,
Old gone John had a habit of biting thumbs,
Old gone John was gone so soon,
Old gone John was called a loon,
Old gone John died one day,
Old gone John will be remembered all the way.

Chelsea Walker (10)
Fallin Primary School, Fallin

Football

Football is good, better than any other sport,
Lots of other people are footballers and it's not boring,
It's amazing!
So don't sit on your bum and do nothing,
Go football mad and it will put a joy on your face.

Kevin O'Hara (10)
Fallin Primary School, Fallin

Football

I don't think football is tragic,
I think football is magic,
Some people think it is sad,
But I go football mad!

Alexander Thomson (10)
Fallin Primary School, Fallin

Working Hard

Working hard as a miner,
Being such a good provider,
A heart of gold and being bold,
Has helped us pull together.

Rachel Marion Landsborough (9)
Fallin Primary School, Fallin

My Mother

Beautiful mother, how sweet can you be?
You're so beautiful, I wish I could be you,
You're so lovely and magical too.

Leah McMeechan (10)
Fallin Primary School, Fallin

The Loch Ness Monster

The scary, strong, enormous Loch Ness monster,
The scary, strong, enormous Loch Ness monster swimming,
The scary, strong, enormous Loch Ness monster swimming gently,
The scary, strong, enormous Loch Ness monster
            swimming gently through the Loch Ness lake,
The scary, strong, enormous Loch Ness monster swimming gently
            through the beautiful Loch Ness lake.

Brandon Miller (9)
Ferryhill Primary School, Edinburgh

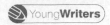
The Thistle

The thistle
The sharp, long, purple thistle
The sharp, long, purple thistle swaying
The sharp, long, purple thistle swaying proudly
The sharp, long, purple thistle swaying proudly
in the rainy Scottish Highlands
The sharp, long, purple thistle swaying proudly
In the wet, rainy Scottish Highlands.

Kevin Glancy (9)
Ferryhill Primary School, Edinburgh

The Soldiers

The soldiers
The powerful, strong, military soldiers
The powerful, strong, military soldiers representing
The powerful, strong, military soldiers representing proudly
The powerful, strong, military soldiers representing proudly
in the Scottish wars
The powerful, strong, military soldiers representing proudly
in the aggressive Scottish wars.

Steven Houston (9)
Ferryhill Primary School, Edinburgh

The Beautiful Thistle

The thistle,
The jaggy, small, beautiful thistle,
The jaggy, small beautiful thistle swaying,
The jaggy, small, beautiful thistle swaying happily,
The jaggy, small, beautiful thistle swaying happily in
the green fields,
The jaggy, small, beautiful thistle swaying happily in
the green summer fields.

Mhari McWiliams (9)
Ferryhill Primary School, Edinburgh

The Loch Ness Monster

The Loch Ness monster,
The huge, long, green Loch Ness monster,
The huge, long, green Loch Ness monster swimming,
The huge, long, green Loch Ness monster swimming quickly,
The huge, long, green Loch Ness monster swimming
quickly under the sea,
The huge, long, green Loch Ness monster swimming quickly
under the deep, blue sea.

Ross Robertson (9)
Ferryhill Primary School, Edinburgh

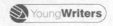
The Loch Ness Monster

The slimy, wavy, scary monster,
The slimy, wavy, scary monster camouflaged,
The slimy, wavy, scary monster, camouflaged proudly,
The slimy, wavy, scary monster camouflaged proudly,
          hiding under the sea,
The slimy, wavy, scary monster camouflaged proudly,
        hiding under the deep, blue sea.

Natasha Semple (9)
Ferryhill Primary School, Edinburgh

The Scottish Army

The brave, strong, respected army,
The brave, strong, respected army fights,
The brave, strong, respected army fights proudly,
The brave, strong, respected army fights proudly with
          all their strength,
The brave, strong, respected army fights proudly with all their
          mighty strength.

Neil De Souza (10)
Ferryhill Primary School, Edinburgh

The Loch Ness Monster

The monster
The long, clumsy, filthy monster,
The long, clumsy, filthy monster sneaking,
The long, clumsy, filthy monster sneaking slowly,
The long, clumsy, filthy monster sneaking slowly into caves,
The long, clumsy, filthy monster sneaking slowly into dark,
creepy caves.

Melissa Sutherland (9)
Ferryhill Primary School, Edinburgh

The Kilt

The colourful, jaggy, thin kilts
The colourful, jaggy, thin kilts folding
The colourful, jaggy, thin kilts folding neatly
The colourful, jaggy, thin kilts folding neatly for another
Scottish day
The colourful, jaggy, thin kilts folding neatly for another
Scottish day up on the highlands.

Kieran Dornan (9)
Ferryhill Primary School, Edinburgh

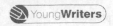

Shortbread

The shortbread,
The tasty, sweet, lovely shortbread,
The tasty, sweet, lovely shortbread sitting,
The tasty, sweet, lovely shortbread sitting cheerfully
on the square plate,
The tasty, sweet, lovely shortbread, sitting cheerfully
on the square, warm plate.

Lucy Orr (9)
Ferryhill Primary School, Edinburgh

The Thistle

The thistle,
The prickly, purple, long thistle,
The prickly, purple, long thistle swaying,
The prickly, purple, long thistle swaying joyfully,
The prickly, purple, long thistle swaying joyfully in the Highlands,
The prickly, purple, long thistle swaying joyfully in the windy,
wet Highlands.

Natalie White (9)
Ferryhill Primary School, Edinburgh

The Saltire

The brave, important, aggressive saltire,
The brave, important, aggressive saltire representing,
The brave, important, aggressive saltire representing strongly,
The brave, important, aggressive saltire representing
                strongly as our Scottish flag,
The brave, important, aggressive saltire representing
                strongly as our beautiful Scottish flag.

Kerry McGee (9)
Ferryhill Primary School, Edinburgh

The Thistle

The spiky, green, purple thistle,
The spiky, green, purple thistle presenting,
The spiky, green, purple thistle presenting proudly,
The spiky, green, purple thistle presenting proudly in the highlands,
The spiky, green, purple thistle presenting proudly
                in the beautiful highlands.

Tierney Hughes (9)
Ferryhill Primary School, Edinburgh

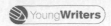

The Scottish Man

The thin, smelly, old Scottish man,
The thin, smelly, old Scottish man walking,
The thin, smelly, old Scottish man walking slowly,
The thin, smelly, old Scottish man walking slowly smoking a pipe,
The thin, smelly, old Scottish man walking slowly smoking a
                                                    brown pipe.

Brooke May (9)
Ferryhill Primary School, Edinburgh

The Thistle

The colourful, spiky, long thistle,
The colourful, spiky, long thistle moving,
The colourful, spiky, long thistle moving proudly,
The colourful, spiky, long thistle moving proudly on a mountain,
The colourful, spiky, long thistle moving proudly on a big,
                                                    green mountain.

Caitlin Cameron (9)
Ferryhill Primary School, Edinburgh

The Castle

The tall, beautiful, grey castle,
The tall, beautiful, grey castle stood,
The tall, beautiful, grey castle stood tall,
The tall, beautiful, grey castle stood tall every day and night,
The tall, beautiful, grey castle stood tall every day and night,
                                        the castle stood alone

Abbie Blackie (9)
Ferryhill Primary School, Edinburgh

Robert Burns

The young, strong poet Robert,
The young, strong poet Robert sang,
The young, strong poet Robert sang beautifully,
The young, strong poet Robert sang beautifully in his house,
The young, strong poet Robert sang beautifully in his thatched
house.

Sophie Cunningham (9)
Ferryhill Primary School, Edinburgh

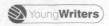

The Soldiers

The brave, brilliant, hard soldiers,
The brave, brilliant, hard soldiers attacking,
The brave, brilliant, hard soldiers attacking safely,
The brave, brilliant, hard soldiers attacking, safely stop the fighting,
The brave, brilliant, hard soldiers attacking, safely stop the
aggressive fighting.

Jonathan Sutherland (9)
Ferryhill Primary School, Edinburgh

The Loch Ness Monster

The big, scary, lonely monster,
The big, scary, lonely monster swimming,
The big, scary, lonely monster swimming proudly,
The big, scary, lonely monster swimming proudly looking for food,
The big, scary, lonely monster swimming proudly,
looking for slimy and scaly food.

Anthony Rodgers (9)
Ferryhill Primary School, Edinburgh

The Flying Unicorn

Unicorn
Quiet, gentle
Sparkly white fur
Pretty, beautiful, magical creature
Wings, flying above
Soft, kind
Wonderful.

Anne Leslie (11)
Cramond Primary School, Edinburgh

Spring Has Sprung

The sun shone down with a rainbow of colours,
As a woollen cloud as white as snow glided by,
The fields were as green as the newly fresh clovers
                    that blew in the wind,
Sheep and lambs, softer than golden feathers
                    hopped about in the powerful sun,
Snow melts on the highest, coldest frozen peaks of mountains.

Greg Glen Muir (11)
Cramond Primary School, Edinburgh

The Haggis

The hot, spicy, black haggis,
The hot, spicy, black haggis sitting,
The hot, spicy, black haggis sitting joyfully,
The hot, spicy, black haggis sitting joyfully on my plate,
The hot, spicy, black haggis sitting joyfully on my pink plate.

Caitlin McKinnon (9)
Ferryhill Primary School, Edinburgh

The Scots

The tall, strong, proud Scots,
The tall, strong, proud Scots danced,
The tall, strong, proud Scots danced cheerfully,
The tall, strong, proud Scots danced cheerfully in their kilts,
The tall, strong, proud Scots danced cheerfully in their tartan kilts.

Jack Carlin (9)
Ferryhill Primary School, Edinburgh

If I Were A Fish

I would live deep below the water
Swimming free with . . .
No hook to get me,
I'd be smooth, bright and mighty
With lots of friends.

Help!
A ship has come
To give some pain
To the fish of the sea.
I'll hide in the coral.

Hurry!

No!

Help!

The hook has got me,
Swordfish come . . .
Come save me.

Hurry!

Now I'm free as can be,
Happy fish - that's me!

Emma McGraw (9)
Gylemuir Primary School, Edinburgh

If I Were A Fish

I would dart around as fast as a fox,
Shimmer, gleam, sparkle and swim,
Amazing lights all around in the deep, dark ocean.

There are friendly plants and careful crabs,
They always like to dance with me and my friends in France,
I like to say they have to pay in the deep, dark ocean.

Me and my friends, we like to go around the bends,
That never seem to have an end in the deep, dark ocean.
My favourite wish, I have to tell,
Is that I am a wonderful fish,
Big or small, I do not care,
In the deep, dark ocean.

Kyle Marshall (9)
Gylemuir Primary School, Edinburgh

If I Were A Fish

If I were a fish . . .
I would swim at the speed of a car
My scales would shine like the shimmering star
I would dive into the ocean
In a wonderful motion
My scales would be shades of green and blues
Like a pair of shiny shoes
I would twirl and twirl and twirl and twirl
But make sure that I don't *hurl!*

Britney Heron (9)
Gylemuir Primary School, Edinburgh

If I Were A Fish

If I were a fish, I would feel free wherever I went,
If i were a fish, I would swim slow,
If I were a fish, I would glitter my scales,
If I were a fish, I would leave a bubbly trail,
If I were a fish, I would stay away from a whale's tail,
If I were a fish, I would swim away from *all* the whales,
If I were a fish, I would have fun,
Especially with my mum.

Abigail Corinne Campbell (9)
Gylemuir Primary School, Edinburgh

If I Were A Fish!

If I were a fish,
I would swim as fast as a bullet from a gun,
I would shimmer like a star,
I would swim and be free and have fun,
I am a rainbow fish
And when the sun shimmers on me,
I am like another sun!

Darby Bunts (9)
Gylemuir Primary School, Edinburgh

If I Were A Fish

If I were a fish
I would be as light, as bright as a star
I would swim as fast as a racing car
My scales would shine as bright as a disco ball
My friends and family love me all
My friends all blend in with the sea
But I'm not a fish, I'm just me!

Sarah Wall (9)
Gylemuir Primary School, Edinburgh

If I Were A Fish

If I were a fish, a smooth and slimy fish,
Moving swiftly in the sea,
The water would be so cold, deep and dark,
It would remind me of ice cream,
It would be fun - freedom!
But lonely, very, very lonely,
I could see sea spiders.

Justin Szabo (9)
Gylemuir Primary School, Edinburgh

If I Were A Fish

If I were a fish, I'd splish and I'd splash,
If I were a fish, I'd be tough and rough,
So I wouldn't end up on a dish with other innocent fish and
I'd splash and I'd dash and escape in a flash,
I'd fight through water all day and all night,
I'd just love to be a fish.

Owen Cruickshank (9)

Gylemuir Primary School, Edinburgh

Happiness

H appiness makes you feel invincible,
A nd always makes you feel so free!
P erhaps it's because
P eople that make you happy
I n your life
N ever want to see you sad.
E ven if your life is full of
S adness and you're feeling blue,
S tay happy and your worries will drift away.

Lauren Pearson (11)

Kilbowie Primary School, Clydebank

Evil Brother

Nose-picker,
Sock-stealer,
CD-scratcher,
Channel-changer,
Hamster-killer,
Room-messer,
Sweet-stealer,
Love him really.

Chelsea Pollock (11)
Kilbowie Primary School, Clydebank

Scotland — Cinquain

Scotland,
Bonnie Scotland,
We are famous for gold,
Our national dress is tartan,
Brave Scots!

William Cowie (11)
Kilbowie Primary School, Clydebank

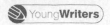
What Is The Moon?

The moon is a silver coin
Glittering in the deep, dancing sky

The moon is a snowball
Spinning in the pitch-black sky

The moon is a shining
Face looking after the world

The moon is a giant cheese
Moulding in a dark cupboard

The moon is a grey rock
Exploding from a volcano

The moon is a glittering crystal
Being turned into a ring

The moon is a big light
Powered by life.

Connor Hillard (10)
Kilchoan Primary School, Kilchoan

What Is The Moon?

The moon is a white snowball
being tossed through the air.

It is a balloon that is lost in
the fairground.

It is a silver pearl trapped
in a dark clam.

It is an empty plate on a dark
tablecloth.

It is a silk, sad, silver face
crying silver tears.

It is a coin being dropped
into a fountain.

It is a light that
brightens the world.

Hannah Hunter (9)
Kilchoan Primary School, Kilchoan

What Is The Moon?

The moon is a grey, glowing ball
Dancing in a deep, dark loch.

It is twinkling in the sky
It is a ship sailing across the sea.

It is a slice of melon floating across the sky
Watching you.

It is being blown across the sky
Glittering, gleaming at the world.

It is a snowball
Floating in the deep, dark sky.

It is a happy face,
Smiling in the sky.

Kirstyn Rowantree (7)
Kilchoan Primary School, Kilchoan

What Is The Moon?

The moon is a grey clock
Gliding through the night.

The moon is nosy
Following you where you go.

The moon is a big, grey rock
Sailing in the sky.

The moon is a balloon
Floating in the air.

The moon is a melon
Carved into a crescent.

Jordan MacLachlan (10)
Kilchoan Primary School, Kilchoan

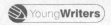
The Desert War

He heard rapid fire,
Bullets whistled past his chest,
He bravely stood his guard,
Thinking he was the best.

The tanks grumbled in the sand,
Planes roared over our heads,
Bombs were dropped
And they were blasted to death.

I yelled in disgust
As everyone was ripped to shreds,
Cautiously I hid, and you
Now know me as dead.

David Mark Carr (11)
Kings Road Primary School, Rosyth

Carnival

I was excited
and amazed
at all the flashing lights.
They were as bright
as the moon at night.

The rides went as fast
as a speeding rocket.
Shooting up like
a shooting star
into the moonlit sky.

Antonio McMillan (10)
Knightswood Primary School, Knightswood

The Crab

I went down to the beach one day
And I saw a crab standing on clay.
It came down from the clay and said to me,
'Hey you there, do you like my clay?'
'It's alright!' I replied,
'Alright' screamed the crab and snipped off my toe.
'Ow!' I screamed, 'you little blighter!
I'll squash you dead, I'll make you lighter!'
Then suddenly from out of nowhere,
A random gull came flying over,
'Oh no!' screamed the crab, 'Oh help me please!'
'Na,' I called, sprinting for some trees.
The gull swooped down and picked up the crab,
'Ha, ha,' I laughed,
'How does he like that?'
Apart from that, the day was dull,
And I owe it all to that random gull!

Magnus Walker (10)
Knightswood Primary School, Knightswood

Young Man from Dundee

There was a young man from Dundee,
Who was always losing his keys,
He looked high and looked low,
Even under the snow,
And he found them, hooray, yippee!

Tyler Grant (10)
Knightswood Primary School, Knightswood

Space

The moon shines bright
Like a fire in the sky,
Spaceships with people,
Flying by.

Other worlds, spinning and turning
Like a tornado spinning around,
Rockets fly up and up,
Looking at the big, black sky.

Ceilidh Murray (10)
Knightswood Primary School, Knightswood

My Brother

His face was like an angel
I felt so very proud
To have a little brother like that
I just wanted to scream out loud
He was like a cute bunny
With blue sparkly eyes
And a big red smile
His name is Ross.

Chloe Dunlop (10)
Knightswood Primary School, Knightswood

Heaven

Heaven sounds like . . . angels singing on a fluffy cloud
Heaven feels like . . . a smooth pillow on my cheek
Heaven smells like . . . sweet roses on a summer day
Heaven tastes like . . . lovely chocolate melting in your mouth
Heaven looks like . . . diamonds shimmering in the sky.

Robert Rutherford (10)
Knightswood Primary School, Knightswood

Blue

Blue is like the sea,
sparkling in the sun.

Blue is like a bluebell,
swaying in the gale.

Blue is like the sky,
in the middle of the day.

Blue is like our school jumper,
hanging on the line.

Blue is like a Ranger's top,
blowing in the wind.

Blue is like a blueberry,
juicy and sweet.

Blue is like mould,
growing on the bread.

Jamie Campbell (11)
Luss Primary School, Luss

The Writer Of This Poem

(Inspired by Roger McGough's 'The Writer of this Poem')

The writer of this poem,
Is shorter than a car,
He likes to watch TV,
And can run very far.

As hairy as a beast,
As smelly as socks,
As keen as my friends,
And likes to wear crocks.

As cheery as Mrs Antonelli,
As smart as a computer,
As lovely as Dannii Minogue,
And as thick as a shooter.

The writer of this poem,
Is as fabulous as can be,
He's run out of words,
So he'll have a cup of tea.

Thomas Robertson (11)
Luss Primary School, Luss

The Writer Of This Poem

(Inspired by Roger McGough's 'The Writer of this Poem')

The writer of this poem
Is shorter than a cupboard,
Faster than Bethan,
Strong as a wrestler.

Funny like a clown,
Smarter than a monkey,
Smaller than tall people,
Cool like Thomas.

The writer of this poem
Hopes the poem will please,
The best in all the world,
He likes a bit of cheese.

Ché Gwilt (8)

Luss Primary School, Luss

Red

Red is like a rose,
round the world.

Red is like love hearts,
on a card.

Red is like apples,
sweet and crunchy.

Red is like strawberries,
shining in the sun.

Red is like tomatoes,
red and ripe.

Bethan Marsh (9)

Luss Primary School, Luss

Apples

Apples,
lovely, shiny,
crunchy, juicy, clean,
mmmmmm delicious.
Apples.

Red apples,
tasty, delightful,
wonderful, glorious,
mmmmmm scrumptious.
Red apples.

Beinn Frame (9)

Luss Primary School, Luss

Winter

Snow
Clean, new, beautiful,
Cool, lovely,
Good fun,
Snow.

Frost
Bitter, freezing,
Wet, hard, cold,
So hard to fall on,
Frost.

Hamish Johnson (8)
Luss Primary School, Luss

A Tapir Is . . .

A scared old man, always watching and ever cautious,
Befuddled, peering out from the bushes,
A lemony yellow, calm and gentle,
A lumpy potato, boring and ordinary,
A bruised orange, round and full of surprises,
A rowing boat, speeding stealthily down the Amazon,
Moomintroll, blobby and cute,
A tulip, plain but beautiful,
A nursery, happy and soft,
A teddy bear, sweet and harmless,
A W standing still,
A rainy day, grey and dull.

Leonie Thorpe (11)
Marybank Primary School, Muir of Ord

A Sloth Is...

An old grandad eating his food in slow motion,
A kiwi with lumpy furry bits,
A desert with slow wind in the summer,
A dead, old sunflower turning grey each second,
A beetle holding up the traffic on the busy motorway,
A statue with cracks making T shapes,
Antiques Roadshow taking forever,
A grey, old, gloomy animal, living in the rainforest.

James Davison (11)
Marybank Primary School, Muir of Ord

A Poison Dart Frog Is

A jumpy boy jumping about,
A sport shop in a sporty place,
A broken couch bending over,
A happy, happy mood on a nice day,
A multicoloured rainbow on a fresh day,
A number one with sticky out legs,
A red onion with peeling off bits,
A green apple rolling around.

Beth Cushnie (8)
Marybank Primary School, Muir of Ord

A Jaguar Is . . .

A samurai, stealthy and strong,
A war zone, always alert,
A monster truck, hefty and fast,
Orange, full of fiery might,
A mace, heavy and sharp,
Determination, nothing's going to stop him,
James Bond, agile and secretive,
Alex Rider, a spy all on his own.

Iain Moodie (10)
Marybank Primary School, Muir of Ord

A Lizard Is . . .

A camouflaged army soldier,
A dark green,
A dark number one, long and thin,
A leek with green frills,
An apple, black and green,
A speeding Zonda flashing across the line,
A Venus flytrap ready to snap with its tongue.

Cameron Harper (10)
Marybank Primary School, Muir of Ord

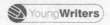
Jaguar Is . . .

A number one stretched and sleek when running,
A racing Mustang first to the finish line,
A dragon fruit ready to fire,
A zoo waiting to attack,
A dragon starting to fly,
A thunder crash in the night.

Megan Gair (10)
Marybank Primary School, Muir of Ord

A Chimp Is . . .

Tesco on a busy Sunday,
A dragon fruit, juicy and spiky,
Happiness, always full of fun,
A number 8 with legs and a curly tail,
A slinky hanging upside down,
An amber ring of fur.

Grace Stewart Skinner (9)
Marybank Primary School, Muir of Ord

A Toucan Is...

A banana, yellow and bent,
A blooming rose, bursting with colour,
A joker, dancing around the room,
Herbie the crazy car, flying through the air,
Sesame Street with bright yellow Big Bird,
White, bright and happy.

Gregor McCormick (10)
Marybank Primary School, Muir of Ord

A Snake Is...

A green celery, long and thin
A long twig, floating down the river
A train slithering down the track
The sly joker
A scary TV programme
A rope coiled in a nest.

Gregor McCarthy (8)
Marybank Primary School, Muir of Ord

A Frog Is . . .

A blue river on a sunny day,
A number four crouching on the ground,
A bouncy ball two metres high,
A happy sun on a summer's day,
A racing Mini speeding around,
A red tulip standing proud.

Rory Owen (9)
Marybank Primary School, Muir of Ord

A Jaguar Is . . .

A jaguar is black anger, ready to attack
A jaguar is a Lamborghini racing at lightning speed
Is a Venus flytrap, nasty and sharp
Is Dennis the Menace, mean and hard
Is a school boy ready to eat.

Mitchell Munro (9)
Marybank Primary School, Muir of Ord

Rainforest Simile Poem

Water as rough as a fish's scales on a sunny day in the rainforest,
Heat as hot as lava in a volcano on a hot summer's day,
Snake as long as a hose coming out of a fire truck,
Trees as tall as a skyscraper in New York.

Zack Benzie (9)
Marybank Primary School, Muir of Ord

School

I love school,
It is really cool,
We stretch the clay,
And we always play,
We do our maths,
And get on with class,
We do our language,
Then it's time for a sandwich,
We do our music,
And learn some songs,
We do our art,
All of us do different parts,
Then it is the end of the day,
Then we can go out and play.

Katie Donaldson (8)
Mount Vernon Primary School, Mount Vernon

Animal Fun

Animals are swinging, animals are having fun
They always like to run in the sun
Monkeys are swinging in the trees in a happy breeze
And birds are away, up high in the sky
Elephants are stomping everywhere to try and give you a scare
All the animals are going to bed
And they are always fed
So bye-bye and go to bed.

Aimee Taggart (8)
Mount Vernon Primary School, Mount Vernon

The Dog

My dog is fluffy,
It's furry and very puffy.
It's funny but it doesn't go near honey.
I take it to the park,
And stay until it's dark.
When my dog goes near a cat,
They both would fight.
When I fly my kite,
My dog would jump and bite.
My dog likes ice cream and chocolate,
When I give him that,
He eats all of it!

Declan Rennie (8)
Mount Vernon Primary School, Mount Vernon

Friends

Friends are special,
Friends are kind,
They never leave you behind,
They're never mean to you,
They share their snacks with you too,
If you're down or feeling blue,
They will always come to cheer you up too,
Together we are strong,
And we will always get along,
We always share our toys and
Chat and make some noise.

Milly Shepherd (8)
Mount Vernon Primary School, Mount Vernon

Castles And Knights

Castles are big, knights are brave,
Sometimes dragons sleep in a cave,
Turrets are tall,
Windows are small,
Murder holes are scary,
It's very hairy,
People fight from the turret,
And people fight back.

Hannah Gibson (8)
Mount Vernon Primary School, Mount Vernon

The Dogs

D ogs, dogs, you are so lovely,
O pen up your hearts and listen to me,
G ive me a hug and give me a lick,
S o then you will be a star!

Liam Reid (8)
Mount Vernon Primary School, Mount Vernon

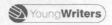

My Heart's In The Highlands

My heart's in the highlands, with rivers that flow,
I love seeing the fish swim in a row,
My heart's in the highlands, with fields so green,
My heart's in the highlands, where the people ain't mean.

My heart's in the highlands, with Nessie I see,
My heart's in the highlands, foxes are chasing me,
My heart's in the highlands, my heart's always there,
My heart's in the highlands, chasing the deer.

My heart's in the highlands, birds soaring above,
My heart's in the highlands, the place that I love.

Kevin MacKay (10)
Obsdale Primary School, Alness

My Cat

Arm-biter,
Food-eater,
Fat thing,
Tree-climber,
Black tail,
Sharp claws,
Dog-scarer,
Lazy lump,
Guinea pig friend,
One black ball of fur.

Adele Mitchell (11)
Obsdale Primary School, Alness

My Cat

Long whiskers,
Shiny eyes,
Sleepy head,
Fast runner,
Mouse lover,
Toy player,
Tree climber,
Soft thing,
Fish eater,
A cuddly friend.

Sumer MacPhee (9)
Obsdale Primary School, Alness

The Doctor

Blue box
Dalek fighter
Time traveller
War stopper
Earth saver
Two hearts
Time lord
Time war
Werewolf
A true hero.

Struan Brown (10)
Obsdale Primary School, Alness

My Heart's In The Highlands

My heart's in the highlands, wherever I go
My heart's in the highlands, all covered in snow
My heart's in the highlands, birds fly up so high
My heart's in the highlands, so high in the sky.

My heart's in the highlands, with lots of mountains
My heart's in the highlands, but there are no fountains
I hear the sound of children having fun
My heart's in the highlands, I smell yummy buns.

Shania Discombe (9)
Obsdale Primary School, Alness

My Heart's In The Highlands

My heart's in the highlands, the misty clouds are high,
My heart's in the highlands, the birds soaring in the sky,
My heart's in the highlands, where I want to be,
My heart's in the highlands, over the watery sea.

My heart's in the highlands, over the loch,
My heart's in the highlands, oh look at that broch,
My heart's in the highlands, with foxes and deer,
My heart's in the highlands, I always want to be here.

Lillian Clark (8)
Obsdale Primary School, Alness

Scotland

S cottie dogs are very funny and dainty,
C astles sit like soldiers on top of the hills,
O utside games, playing tig, getting out,
T histles are very jabby,
L och Ness monster,
A nd lovely, creamy ice cream cones,
N essie, the Loch Ness monster,
D ingwall is a very good place.

Andrew Fowler (8)

Obsdale Primary School, Alness

Scotland

S cottish haggis - meaty, beefy food,
C old hills in the north of Scotland,
O utdoor sports - climbing bumpy hills,
T histles are very spiky plants,
L och Ness monster is very famous to Scotland,
A berdeen is famous for hard stones and oil industries,
N ine or eighteen holes are challenging courses,
D undee, a special city, not so good at their football!

David Manson (8)

Obsdale Primary School, Alness

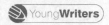

Scotland

S cottie dogs are so white like snow, black ones are like cold nights,
C old when night, so don't get a fright,
O n Scotland we eat haggis and shortbread,
T histles may hurt you but they are beautiful to see,
L och Ness is famous for Nessie, the Loch Ness monster,
A nd highland cows are so hairy,
N arrow rivers winding down the hills,
D own in Scotland there is Edinburgh Castle.

Samantha Sutherland (9)
Obsdale Primary School, Alness

Scotland

S cottish kilts are very Scottish,
C old days up frosty hills,
O ats you put into your porridge,
T histle is a Scottish stingy flower,
L ovely Scottie dogs I see outside,
A ngus is a very Scottish name,
N essie is a very friendly dinosaur,
D ingwall is down a hill.

Emily Taylor (8)
Obsdale Primary School, Alness

Scotland

S cotland's castles,
C old winds blow in Scotland,
O utdoor sports in the cold, fresh air,
T histles, spiky and tall, blowing,
L och Ness the home of our Nessie,
A haggis running around the hills,
N essie, our friendly monster,
D rums and pipe bands, big loud noises.

Murdo Maclean (9)
Obsdale Primary School, Alness

Friends

Friends,
Look around,
They are everywhere,
You've got tonnes of them,
So look around,
They're here,
Hooray!

Alan Macled (11)
Obsdale Primary School, Alness

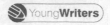

The Lion

Animal,
Big spots,
Really sharp claws.
Chases after its prey,
Big, bushy mane,
Can kill,
Big.

Tyler Buchan (11)
Obsdale Primary School, Alness

My Cat

Cat,
Pointy ears,
Lots of whiskers,
Likes wrecking my things,
A fast striker,
Moves fast,
Cat.

Amy Manson (9)
Obsdale Primary School, Alness

The Snake

Slithery,
Slimy skin,
A small head,
They are good at hiding,
A mice eater,
Shady skin.

Allanis Stirling (11)
Obsdale Primary School, Alness

My Heart's In The Highlands

My heart's in the highlands, wherever I go,
My heart's in the highlands, all covered in snow.

I see a big river, with little fish,
I see a big river, with Nessie, I wish.

Dylan Taylor (8)
Obsdale Primary School, Alness

My Heart's In The Highlands

My heart's in the highlands, all covered in snow,
My heart's in the highlands, birds flying so low,
My heart's in the highlands, with bees flying by me,
My heart's in the highlands, my family beside me.

Gary Wilson (9)
Obsdale Primary School, Alness

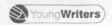
My Heart's In The Highlands

My heart's in the highlands, my heart is here,
When I look around me, I see lots of deer,
My heart's in the highlands, I'm in a canoe,
My heart's in the highlands, I hear a coo.

Errin Longbotham (10)
Obsdale Primary School, Alness

My Dog

My dog is called Candy,
She is white and brown,
She is fine and dandy,
She never has a frown.

Candy is so cute,
But she can be a pest,
She always eats my food,
But she is the best.

She has a pink lead,
She pulls me all the time,
She is a pain in the head,
But she is all mine.

She only is a puppy,
She is not very tall,
She is so muddy,
She is so small.

Erin Gallacher (10)
Our Lady of Loretto Primary School, Dalmuir

Underwater Rap

I was swimming in the water,
And I saw a shark,
And I listened again,
And I heard a fish bark.

The fish goes woof, woof,
The shark goes raar,
The fish goes loof, loof,
The shark swims far.

I'm swimming along,
And I'm singing a song,
Then I see the fish,
And it's in a dish.

The shark is gone,
And it's such a con,
Cause it stole my money,
And it wasn't funny.

The fish comes back,
And it's holding a sack,
It's got my money,
And it's got a bunny.

This is my story,
I hope it wasn't gorey,
It's a great tale,
And it's never gonna fail.

Matthew McGurk (10)
Our Lady of Loretto Primary School, Dalmuir

Winter Poem

Frosty grass and hills
are white and
beautiful.
Twinkly
spiders' webs.
It's chilly
outside as the
children play.
Snowy all around us
as we make snowmen.
Icy grounds
are slippy when
we walk on them.
Freezing
weather everywhere.
Rainy all the time
and makes the snow slush.
Blowy trees
turning white
from the frost.
Misty places
as you go about.
Foggy as you see
the headlights from cars.

Ashly Meehan (10)
Our Lady of Loretto Primary School, Dalmuir

My Dog Diabla

My dog Diabla is so wild,
She jumps around the dinner table like a wild hound.

My dog Diabla is so wild,
And she's always after a child,
She hunted down a bunny,
And roasted it with honey.
Once she ran away,
That was not OK,
I was sobbing,
But my little brother was hopping,
Well I still have my cat,
Who is so black,
My cat Nightshade,
Should be called Frightshade,
She's a really good cat,
But she's a bit fat,
She beats up the cats,
That beat up my old cat,
These are the things I love about my pet
And the things I will never forget.

Max Porter (8)
Our Lady of Loretto Primary School, Dalmuir

My Winter Poem

Footsteps crunching deep in snow,
Children's faces beaming aglow,
Scarves and hats and happy faces,
Oh, how the snow was high in places,
Big decorations and Christmas trees,
Shivery arms and knobbly knees.

Presents, presents under the tree,
Oh, I wonder which one is for me!
Family chatting at the door,
I scatter my presents all over the floor,
Dancing, prancing, jumping around,
That's what Christmas is all about.

Dinner, dinner, oh what I love to eat!
Stuffing, turkey and lots of meat,
Laughing, chatting, talking tonight,
It really makes me feel alright,
Then I'm full, I've had enough,
That's why I love Christmas so much!

Taylor Docherty (10)
Our Lady of Loretto Primary School, Dalmuir

My Cat

I have a cat
But he's always sleepy
He's really fat
He's always leapy.

He really beats me up
I like my cat
He gives me good luck
And he always wears my hat.

My cat is called Mandy
She is black
She loves to eat candy
She lies on my back.

When she is good,
She is OK
When she's calmed down, I give her some food
She is really homey.

Eryn Burns (8)
Our Lady of Loretto Primary School, Dalmuir

Guinea Pigs

You can get small ones, fat ones and skinny ones too,
Fat, skinny or small,
They can run, jump and also squeak for food,
When the food runs out,
Guinea pigs are cool and they think they rule,
They smell a little and it's cute when they're sleeping.

Zoe Rankin (10)
Our Lady of Loretto Primary School, Dalmuir

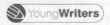

Our Eco Committee

O is for our world,
U is for us against the world,
R is for the rain.

E is for Eco Committee,
C is for carbon omissions,
O is for our solar system.

C is for cuddly polar bears that are in danger,
O is for our responsibility,
M is for Mother Nature we need to preserve,
M is for mistreating our resources,
I is for important issues that need to be looked at,
T is for time running out,
T is for treating our world better,
E is for everyone taking part,
E is for everyone is doing the right thing.

Erin Hawthorne (10)
Our Lady of Loretto Primary School, Dalmuir

Dog

My dog is so cool,
And he is very small,
He acts like a bull,
Sometimes he's like a fluffy ball.

He loves it in the rain,
Sometimes when he has food,
He wants to go on a train,
Then he goes into a mood.

When he is outside,
He sits beside me,
He likes to go to the seaside,
And he hates bees.

He likes to go for a walk,
And likes to read a book.

Ryan Hepburn (8)
Our Lady of Loretto Primary School, Dalmuir

Wintry World

Shiny, glittery ice glistening,
Joyful children having fabulous fun,
Snowmen made out of sparkling snow,
Winter is back, is that so?

It's this spectacular season,
Sliding, slippy ice,
Sledging, having snowball fights,
It's back to our wintry world.

Shannon McKinlay (10)
Our Lady of Loretto Primary School, Dalmuir

Snails

Snails,
Snails, snails,
They are so slow,
It would take them
All day to get themselves home,
Their shells are so hard,
As hard as a brick.

If you stand on me,
I'll be sure to cry,
Their eyes are so small,
You can't even see them right up close,
Snails are like slugs but slugs don't have shells,
They're both really slow! So what can I say?
Snails, snails, snails.

Megan Skeith (10)
Our Lady of Loretto Primary School, Dalmuir

Eryn

Eryn is so funny,
She even likes curry,
When she walks down the hall,
I always say that she is tall,
Her hair is brown,
Her frown is always upside down,
She has a big brother called Liam,
I'll give you a shout if I see him,
I'm in Primary 5 and Eryn is in Primary 4,
But we try our best to get the same score,
We are with each other every day,
We try to get along and play,
She always likes to go a dinner,
In my eyes she's always a winner!

Alana Murray (9)
Our Lady of Loretto Primary School, Dalmuir

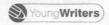

My Teddy

My wee teddy, I love him so,
His name is Scrappy, yes it is,
He is so scruffy and a wee soul,
His best friend is named Chris.

He has lots of hair,
And is dark brown,
He looks like a bear,
He has a funny frown.

I sleep with him at night,
Because he is soft to touch,
I hold him very tight,
Because I love him so much.

Antonia Gillespie (8)
Our Lady of Loretto Primary School, Dalmuir

Eco Links

P eople play in our playground,
L ittle plants in the plant pots inside the compost,
A ll Primary 6's play the Primary 7's, I've tried to beat them,
Y o, yo, yo, this is the Eco School!
G round is clear, we need some shoots to be cool,
R ound the school is our Eco School,
O ur school is cool!
U nder the ground is a pound,
N o! No! No! Our school needs the Green Flag!
D own, down under the ground.

Luke Cadden (11)
Our Lady of Loretto Primary School, Dalmuir

Go Eco!

G o Eco team,
R ecycled paper,
E co all the way,
E veryone can make a difference,
N ever leave lights on.

E xpensive electricity,
C ardboard can be recycled,
O ur world is falling apart.

T ry to recycle,
E ventually the world will be gone,
A lways put litter in the bin,
M ake our world green.

Callum Granger (10)
Our Lady of Loretto Primary School, Dalmuir

Rainforest — Haikus

Monkeys have a land
It is called a rainforest
They always swing there.

Rainforests are cool
You can play coconut ball
It is very fun.

Lots of animals
Think I am famous because
I always hunt there.

Dionne Brown (8)
Our Lady of Loretto Primary School, Dalmuir

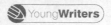

My Winter Poem

I sit watching the passers-by
battling through snow and wind.
Streaming scarves whirling high
hats and heads are low.

I hear, as the dancing snowflakes
flutter all around.
I imagine the tune
as they fall to the glistening ground.

I feel their coldness through the window
as they hurry to wherever they go.
Heavy bags in their hands
struggling through the snow.

Summer Cranney (10)
Our Lady of Loretto Primary School, Dalmuir

Rainforest – Haikus

Racoons are so cute,
Gorillas are so freaky,
Oh mother help me.

Baboons are so cool,
They have red and blue noses,
They are so stupid.

Tigers hunt their food,
Tigers eat deer and insects,
They are so vicious.

Kelsey Young (8)
Our Lady of Loretto Primary School, Dalmuir

My Playground

M y special playground
Y oung children playing

P laying till home-time
L ying down when getting home
A lways having fun
Y oung boys playing on the football pitch
G rounds are very dry
R unning about and having fun
O n our special grounds
U nder the sun
N ever stop having fun
D one, it's now night, goodnight.

Mark Biggins (10)
Our Lady of Loretto Primary School, Dalmuir

Artur Boruc

There once was a fantastic goalie,
He was very bad and extremely holy.
He saved the powerful swerving shots,
But when it came into his thoughts,
He didn't save the powerful swerving shots,
At the end of the season, he didn't save a lot.
He wasn't the best or number one,
Because he was out in the pub having fun.
But one night he wasn't out - what a surprise!
The bad manger was giving him the eyes.
One game he missed out,
And from that day forward, he didn't go out and about.

Ryan Murphy (8)
Our Lady of Loretto Primary School, Dalmuir

Dogs

I love dogs,
Especially their bark,
They jump onto logs,
And their bites leave a mark,
They can be silly creatures,
They chase cars and cats,
They have lots of different features,
They fall asleep on mats,
They love it when you brush their coats,
And tickle behind their ears,
When on rivers, some jump off boats,
And when they die, it leaves me in tears.

Paul Ross (9)
Our Lady of Loretto Primary School, Dalmuir

My Family

My mum is nice,
She knows the price,
My dad is a dude,
And he is good,
My sister is neat,
And she is sweet,
My brother is a pest,
But he's the best!
I love my family,
So, so much,
They are the best,
In all the west!

Chloe Byrne (10)
Our Lady of Loretto Primary School, Dalmuir

Eco Poem

L ights should be turned off,
E co is what we are,
T errible is people who dump litter,
S ave our world

G reen flag is our goal,
O zone layer has many holes

G reen world makes a better place,
R educe, reuse, recycle,
E lectricity is really bad for the world,
E nergy saving,
N uclear power plants pollute our air.

Sarah O'Loughlin (10)
Our Lady of Loretto Primary School, Dalmuir

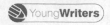
By The Sea

Dolphins diving,
seals splashing,
otters swimming,
in the sea.
Shhh, shhh,
Splash, splash,
Sun setting,
like a big bonfire,
a beautiful night for the lovely sea,
with you and me.

Ellen Johnston (7)

Port Ellen Primary School, Port Ellen

The Harvester

Boats on the surf
Lobster happy in the rock pool
Crabs relaxing in the pool
Clams happy as anything
Creels coming up from the sea
A shoal of fish go by
No rogue waves
Waves crashing on the rocks
Happy days
Fishing on The Harvester.

Jason Baker (7)

Port Ellen Primary School, Port Ellen

Shark Fishing

Out on the sea,
Fishing for sharks,
Fishing rod ready,
Bait in the bucket,
Fin in the distance,
Cast your rod,
Wait . . . wait,
Pull . . . pull,
Help . . . help,
What a catch!

Josh Henderson (7)
Port Ellen Primary School, Port Ellen

The Deep Blue Sea

Down in the deep, blue sea,
dolphins diving behind me,
fish swimming all around,
water crashing and smashing,
seals swimming like fish,
mermaids' tails as gold as rings,
crabs nipping divers,
divers swimming,
jellyfish stinging,
water flowing.

Ruby Miller (7)
Port Ellen Primary School, Port Ellen

Swimming With The Fish

Fish are swimming everywhere,
Like moving leaves,
Starfish lying on the ground,
Like shiny seaweed,
Dolphins jumping up and down,
Having a great time,
Big waves above me,
Shiny shark swimming straight towards me,
Help!

Eilidh McMillan (7)
Port Ellen Primary School, Port Ellen

On A Fishing Boat

At sea in a storm,
Waves crashing over you,
Like a rogue wave,
Pushing you back like a great storm,
Scary like a vampire,
Rolling, bouncing, banging,
Getting tossed up and down
At sea,
In a fishing boat.

Connor Jamieson (7)
Port Ellen Primary School, Port Ellen

By The Calm Sea

Calm sea at the beach,
Waves passing by me,
Seaweed growing like plants,
I can see the mermaid on the rocks,
I can build a sandcastle on the beach,
Lovely, sparkly, sandy shells,
Can you see the fishing boat on the sea?
I can hear the *shh . . . shh . . . shhh,*
The calm sea makes at the beach.

Emily Logan (7)
Port Ellen Primary School, Port Ellen

The Litter Gale

Mean rubbish blowing,
Hungry seagulls eating,
Thoughtless people dropping,
People don't care,
So messy,
Feeling sad and angry,
Animals dying,
Sad world crying,
That's the litter there.

Daniel Smith (8)
Port Ellen Primary School, Port Ellen

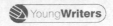

Surfing In Space

Surfing on the sea,
Like an alien ship,
Splash go the waves,
Like tumbling curls,
You have a wavy wash,
Dark blue splashing on your fiery red board,
The water is calm,
Like a flat, smooth flounder.

Scott Kinloch (7)

Port Ellen Primary School, Port Ellen

In The Sea

In the sea
waves going up and down
up and down
plastic bags floating
tin cans bobbing
old creels sinking
message in a bottle
saying, *keep the sea clean!*

Reece Bowman (7)

Port Ellen Primary School, Port Ellen

Lucky Days

Dancing dolphins,
swimming in the deep sea,
shining in the sun,
going in all directions,
diving up and around about,
me swimming in-between,
feeling so lucky,
like I have won the lottery.

Aileas Colthart (8)

Port Ellen Primary School, Port Ellen

Under The Sea

Under the sea,
swimming with fish,
sparkly like jewels,
spotty like ladybirds,
as colourful as rainbows.
Giant turtle swimming by like a mythical creature,
floating gently by on the currents,
under the sea.

Angus MacMillan (8)

Port Ellen Primary School, Port Ellen

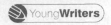

Stormy Streets

Wind blowing,
Sweet wrappers howling,
People dropping litter,
Like they don't care,
A mountain of litter,
So messy,
World getting covered,
In a mountain of waste.

Harry Thomson (8)
Port Ellen Primary School, Port Ellen

Hide-And-Seek

Fish are swimming,
Like a golden bubblebath,
Killer whale chasing them,
Black and white,
Fast like a jet,
The fish split up,
A game of hide-and-seek.

James Adams (7)
Port Ellen Primary School, Port Ellen

Storm At Sea

Surfing in the sea like a shark,
Waves are crashing against the boat,
Jagged rocks like vampire teeth,
Sea so dark like a Hallowe'en bat,
Big waves like a giant,
Wind howling like a wolf.

Ewan MacKinnon (7)
Port Ellen Primary School, Port Ellen

Under The Sea

Under the sea
Clams clapping and
Fish colourful as toys
Swimming happily
Playing hide-and-seek together with
Dolphins splashing about in the waves.

Helen Sinclair (7)
Port Ellen Primary School, Port Ellen

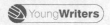

By The Sea

Looking out to sea,
Sea shining like a crystal,
The calm waves roll in,
Splash go the waves,
Dolphins jumping for joy,
I feel happy.

Calum Campbell (7)

Port Ellen Primary School, Port Ellen

Diving

Diving down into the rough sea,
Seeing the boats go by,
Seeing the fish glow in the dark,
Seeing the crabs in the creels,
Jellyfish floating by like bags in the wind.

Donald MacGill (8)

Port Ellen Primary School, Port Ellen

Diving

Daring dolphins diving through the sea,
The green waves roll in.
Shiny seals relaxing on the brown rocks,
Green sea with stormy white horses,
Tangled seaweed swirling softly like snowflakes.

Liam Campbell (7)
Port Ellen Primary School, Port Ellen

Special Friends!

S pecial
P eople
E njoy games
C aring is fun
I love to play
A ll day!
L aughing all the way!

F ull of joy!
R unning around
I n a sunny area!
E verlasting
N ever-ending
D ays are fun
S unshine is with us all day long!

Amy Louise Crook (8)
Raasay Primary School, Isle of Raasay

The Four Seasons — Cinquains

Springtime,
The lambs are born,
All the flowers blossom.
Children go out on sunny days.
Springtime.

Summer,
The sea is warm.
Sun is shining on us.
Go fishing and catch lots of fish.
Summer.

Autumn,
Leaves fall off trees,
They go yellow or brown.
The winds starts to pick up and blow.
Autumn.

Winter,
The trees are bare.
Snow flies and falls on them,
Gales blow things down, so wrap up warm.
Winter.

Rosie MacLeod (10)
Raasay Primary School, Isle of Raasay

My Fish

Water-breather
Bubble-maker
Cat-hater
Tank-cleaner
Good-swimmer
Water-lover
Golden colour
Food-lover
A good fish!

Alastair McGowan (9)

Raasay Primary School, Isle of Raasay

Eco And Pollution

Eco,
Clean, healthy,
Recycling, saving, stopping,
Very friendly to animals and plants,
Killing, destroying, heating,
Dirty, unclean,
Pollution.

Ross Murray Camilli (9)

Raasay Primary School, Isle of Raasay

Diamante Poem

Lions
Fearless, scary
Running, pouncing, eating
Thrashing through the grass, climbing a tree
Laughing, jumping, drinking
Noisy, busy
Humans.

Gabriel Allan David Macleod Carslaw (9)

Raasay Primary School, Isle of Raasay

Sea And Beach

Sea,
Salty, turquoise,
Soaking, shining, twinkling,
The strong current, the soft sand,
Digging, walking, playing,
Soft, sun,
Beach.

Kirsty Nicolson (11)

Raasay Primary School, Isle of Raasay

My Winter Poem – Haiku

Kids making snowballs
To throw at other people
Laughter everywhere.

Robyn Sutherland (8)
Rattray Primary School, Rattray

Winter Fun – Haiku

Snowmen getting made,
It's very icy today,
Children having fun.

Lauren Ritchie (8)
Rattray Primary School, Rattray

Snowy Day – Haiku

Children are sledging,
They are having so much fun,
Cold snowflakes falling.

Katie Robertson (7)
Rattray Primary School, Rattray

My Snowy Haiku

Freezing, icy snow,
Throwing snowballs everywhere,
Sliding happily.

Robyn Milne (8)
Rattray Primary School, Rattray

My Snow Fun – Haiku

The kids are freezing,
Girls are making a snowman,
Boys are throwing snow.

Kaylin McDonald (7)
Rattray Primary School, Rattray

My Winter Poem – Haiku

Kids play in the snow,
Hats, scarves, jackets, keep them warm,
Flinging by snowballs.

Heidi McDonald (8)
Rattray Primary School, Rattray

Snowy Day — Haiku

Slippy kids sliding,
It's very icy today,
Cold children playing.

Natalie Fair (8)
Rattray Primary School, Rattray

My Winter Poem — Haiku

Children are sledging,
Girls are playing in the snow,
Outside it's icy.

Niamh Grant (8)
Rattray Primary School, Rattray

Winter Day — Haiku

Snow is freezing cold,
Children making big snowmen,
Having lots of fun.

Amy Cameron (8)
Rattray Primary School, Rattray

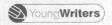
In Winter – Haiku

Kids flinging snowballs,
Slipping on ice, having fun,
Playing in the snow.

Georgina Brown (8)
Rattray Primary School, Rattray

My Winter – Haiku

The kids are playing,
Cold snowflakes are dropping down,
Their fingers frozen.

Dylan Tindal (8)
Rattray Primary School, Rattray

A Snowy Day – Haiku

The kids are frozen,
A snowflake is dropping down,
Boys are throwing snow.

Sammy Metcalf (8)
Rattray Primary School, Rattray

My Haiku Poem

Kids flinging snowballs,
Skiing down an icy slope,
Skidding and sliding.

Andrew King (8)
Rattray Primary School, Rattray

My Winter Poem — Haiku

Kids play in the snow,
Throwing snow and having fun,
What a lovely day.

Gary Dobbin (8)
Rattray Primary School, Rattray

Winter Fun — Haiku

Kids playing with snow,
Children having snowball fights,
It's fun having snow.

Matthew Breen (8)
Rattray Primary School, Rattray

Snowy – Haiku

Throwing big snowballs,
Children playing, having fun,
Laughing in the snow.

Dion Tolmie (8)
Rattray Primary School, Rattray

The Sea

I hear the sound of the waves,
Hit against the sand,
I throw some sand at my friends,
But it keeps slipping off my hands.

I love going to the seaside,
And playing with my friends,
Splashing about in the water,
This fun never ends.

I wish to go to the seaside again,
Because it's so much fun,
I love going on the beach,
And having a little run.

But I haven't been there for ages,
So the sand I cannot touch,
I don't do anything else,
Because I miss the sea too much.

Nicola O'Donnell (9)
St Bridget's Primary School, Baillieston

The Jungle

Jungle, jungle, birds and trees,
Monkeys swinging to tree to tree,
Snakes slithering through the green, green grass,
Rivers and rocks, quicksand too,
Vines and bushes, both green,
Hippos, koalas, both grey,
Little birds, all different colours,
Especially the parrots,
Ucky bugs, ucky mud,
Watch out it might not be mud!

Emily Harkness (10)
St Bridget's Primary School, Baillieston

Football

F ast feet,
O ver the net,
O wn goal,
T hrow in,
B rilliant goal,
A bsolutely brilliant,
L ast minute,
L eft foot.

Rebecca Bailey (9)
St Bridget's Primary School, Baillieston

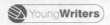

Snow

Light and fluffy, falling from the sky,
Leaving behind a white blanket,
Men of snow with carrot noses,
Angel shapes made on the ground,
Children wrapped up warm and cosy,
Dodging snowballs, sliding, slipping,
Head indoors after lots of fun,
For warm hot chocolate by the fire.

Jude Wallace (9)
St Bridget's Primary School, Baillieston

Princess

P retty princess,
R iding on a horse,
I n her hair, a rose,
N ow the sun will shine,
C astle in the distance,
E vening draws near,
S oon it will be time to go,
S inging all the way.

Emma Boyle (9)
St Bridget's Primary School, Baillieston

Rocket In Space

R ockets everywhere in space,
O ver stars and into planets,
C rash and you might never be seen,
K illed by a comet,
E veryone has to like the atmosphere,
T he Milky Way is great,
S hiny stars are fun to watch.

Ryan Slavin (9)
St Bridget's Primary School, Baillieston

The Sea

Sea,
Sandy waves,
Fishing, floating, swimming,
Jumping seahorses all about,
Hurrying, running, shouting,
Hot, grass,
Land.

Ryan Docherty (9)
St Bridget's Primary School, Baillieston

Untitled

There was a knight called Lancelot,
He really liked to dance a lot,
As he sat on the Round Table,
His horse slept in a stable,
While he ate brunch a lot,
His horse liked to bounce a lot,
That was the tale of Lancelot.

Lauryn Muir
St Bridget's Primary School, Baillieston

The Sea

T he sea is as clear as glass,
H arry went into the ice-cold water,
E nter the freezing cold sea.

S tarfish stick to rocks like glue,
E xcellent water for fish but not for us,
A t the end of the sea, a shark waits for you.

Stephanie Crum (9)
St Bridget's Primary School, Baillieston

The Jungle

J ungle is a dangerous place,
U nder the water crocodiles wait for me,
N ot a safe place a jungle to be,
G etting out of quicksand is a problem for me,
L azy owls come out and catch their prey,
E veryone is scared when a jungle is near.

Calum Neil Alexander (9)
St Bridget's Primary School, Baillieston

Apples

A pples are so healthy,
P retty,
P erfect,
L ike them a lot,
E at them all day,
S o nice.

Tegan Winters (8)
St Bridget's Primary School, Baillieston

Yummy Apples

I like apples, yes I do,
Juicy, hard seeds in them too,
Red apples, green apples,
Big or small,
I like apples,
I'll eat them all day long.

Chloe Watson (8)
St Bridget's Primary School, Baillieston

Princess Mazy And Her Friend The Daisy

Princess Mazy,
Planted a daisy,
And encouraged it to grow.

It grew so high,
It touched the sky,
And had to be chopped down.

The king was mad,
But Princess Mazy was sad,
And cried throughout night and day.

She was going round the bend,
Missing her flower friend,
So she planted another one.

This one was small,
And didn't last long at all,
So Princess Mazy gave up on her gardening.

Fiona Thacker (11)
St Ninian's Primary School, Gourock

My Soul

It's like a falling leaf,
Touched by the wind,
It lands on the stream,
A beautiful divine

Darkness, of light,
Labyrinth, of mind,
A queen, the heard,
Of the invisible,
All the lost

A tear,
Falls fast,
But slow,
Time lasts

A song, the sound,
So bright,
Pain writes,
My song

Some words
Do fade,
But some,
Will stay

Memories are there,
They never leave,
In the horrific battle,
They are your sleep

My soul,
My heart,
The Earth from the sky,
Deep inside me, is where it lies . . .

Lynne Duddy (11)
St Ninian's Primary School, Gourock

Every Day Heroes

People think that heroes,
Are people who can fly,
But heroes can be humans,
Who save people who are about to die.

Doctors and nurses perform operations,
Saving people who need help,
They give jabs and medicines to the nations,
But they need some help.

Firemen and women put out the fires,
To stop our world getting toasted,
They are at risk from the flames,
So we don't get roasted.

Police are out to catch criminals,
They risk lives to help save others,
And put the bad guys in jail,
To put a stop to lots of murders.

Coastguards look after you in the water,
If you're ever in trouble,
You know to holler,
And the coastguard will come to the rescue.

All people have been saved by them,
So that means,
That they are
Heroes!

Ellie Carroll
St Ninian's Primary School, Gourock

Violence

Violence is crime
Violence is hurtful
People survive, but not many
When you sit down you watch the news
You hope to sit and watch something
Glad and new
But all you see is people dying
When you see the killers and then the family
You see the tears
You hear them cry
They say on TV, violence to go by.

Think how many people die
Think how many survive
I don't like the feeling
That it could be me next.

Maybe they are drunk
Maybe they are sober
Maybe it is revenge
Just sort it out!

So you're not next
Tell the police
That someone has hurt you
Tell your mum to help and praise you . . .

Brandon Lee (11)
St Ninian's Primary School, Gourock

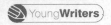

The Future

As I dream at night,
I wonder what this world will be
In 3009!

Lots of three-eyed dogs,
Monkeys with twelve paws,
Teachers don't exist,
Robots take the risk.

Flying cars outside,
Rules they don't abide,
Fish are now extinct,
Because they couldn't blink.

Mirrors all around,
Even on the ground,
I'm feeling so confused,
I am not amused.

And now the story ends,
I'm glad that I'm not one of them,
Back in 2009,
The best year of my life!

Jenna Doyle & Francesca Dempsey (11)
St Ninian's Primary School, Gourock

Nightmares!

I'm scared to go to sleep,
I fight with my mum,
I sit there and weep,

I can't go to sleep!

When she gets me in my bed,
I lie awake,
I speak to myself,
Oh for goodness sake.'

I cannot go to sleep!
I wait for the ghosts to leap in the night,
To wake me up,
And give me a fright,
The banshees scream at the top of their voices.

I cannot get to sleep!

Nightmares made me who I am now,
I'm brave and helpful and I see,
What they did to me!

I can get to sleep!

Carys Knox & Ellie Carroll (11)
St Ninian's Primary School, Gourock

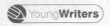

My Pet Dog

My pet dog is called Rover,
He is scared of the Hoover,
He is practically a wimp,
But he's my dog.

My pet dog is Rover,
He likes to have a pat,
But he especially likes to lie on the front door mat.

My pet dog is Rover,
He's a very talented dog,
I have never seen another dog juggle across a muddy bog.

My pet dog is Rover,
I think he's a very special dog,
Not for any certain reason,
But because he's my dog.

Olivia Fleming (11)
St Ninian's Primary School, Gourock

Forgotten

I turn, you're there,
But you don't see me,
It's like I'm invisible,
But not invincible.

Am I like a solid wall?
Taken for granted,
I feel like I'm alone,
I turn again, you're gone.

I feel like I'm falling through darkness,
It begins closing in,
I'm trapped, I shout, but no one's there,
I've always been forgotten.

Liam Turner (11)
St Ninian's Primary School, Gourock

Red

Red is like a crunchy apple,
Red is a juicy cherry,
Red is a red paint pot,
Red tastes like a sweet grape rolling around in my mouth,
Red smells like a sweet strawberry taken straight off a plant,
Red sounds like runny blood going through my body,
Red feels like water going down my throat,
Red looks like a shiny ruby,
Red makes me feel great and the colour of a rose,
Red is my favourite colour.

Aidan Ferguson (8)
St Ninian's Primary School, Gourock

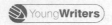

Pink

Pink is a big, pink fluffy cloud floating in the sky.
Pink is Miriam's very bright pink pencil case.
Pink is beautiful pink earrings.
Pink tastes like lovely strawberry jam.
Pink smells like pink prickly roses.
Pink sounds like breathing through your pink lungs.
Pink feels like frilly pink knickers.
Pink looks like a silky pink dress.
Pink makes me feel fantastic!
Pink is my favourite colour!

Abbie O'Donnell (8)
St Ninian's Primary School, Gourock

Red

Red is like a tasty cherry in my mouth,
Red is like a dark colour of paint,
Red is like our desks at school,
Red tastes like a lovely seedy strawberry,
Red smells like a beautiful rose,
Red sounds like a lot of heart beats,
Red feels like red ink dropping onto my hand,
Red looks like a shiny ruby,
Red makes me smile a lot,
Red is my favourite colour.

Hannah Watt (8)
St Ninian's Primary School, Gourock

Gold

Gold is like a shining star glistening in the sky,
Gold is a glimmering, tingling one pound coin,
Gold is a warm caramel bar on a summer's day,
Gold tastes like golden puffs on a hot day,
Gold smells like the morning sun,
Gold sounds like a telescope,
Gold feels like a rattling coin,
Gold looks like a tingling split-pin,
Gold makes me tingle in my body,
Gold is my favourite colour.

Christopher Morris (8)
St Ninian's Primary School, Gourock

White

White is a star in the sky.
White is the snow.
White is a fluffy cloud.
White tastes like marshmallows.
White smells like smoke.
White sounds like a swan.
White feels like tissue paper.
White looks like soft sheep.
White makes me happy.
White is my favourite colour.

Declan McGarrigle (9)
St Ninian's Primary School, Gourock

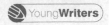

Blue

Blue are the jumping dolphins,
Blue is a lovely bluebell,
Blue is like a sweet blueberry,
Blue tastes like a blue sweet,
Blue smells like a sweet violet,
Blue sounds like the wavy sea,
Blue feels like the wet water,
Blue looks like the clear sky,
Blue makes me think of the people,
Blue is my favourite colour.

Carys Weston (8)
St Ninian's Primary School, Gourock

Blue

Blue are the jumping dolphins,
Blue is the bursting bubbles,
Blue is the noisy whales,
Blue tastes like juicy blueberries,
Blue smells like a sweet violet,
Blue sounds like the wavy water,
Blue feels like thick paint,
Blue looks like our cool school uniform,
Blue makes me happy,
Blue is my favourite colour.

Rachel Robertson (9)
St Ninian's Primary School, Gourock

Blue

Blue is the colour of the wavy sea,
Blue is a juicy blueberry,
Blue is a dolphin jumping out of the water,
Blue tastes like sweet blueberry pie,
Blue smells like a lovely violet,
Blue sounds like the wet water splashing against the shore,
Blue feels like a lovely silk top,
Blue looks like the high sky,
Blue makes me happy,
Blue is my favourite colour.

Louise Turner (8)
St Ninian's Primary School, Gourock

Pink

Pink is like a beautiful rose stuck to the ground,
Pink is like our lungs that help us to breath,
Pink is like a hairband that we can wear,
Pink tastes like sweet strawberry jam,
Pink smells like tasty strawberry ice cream,
Pink sounds like little bits of paint splashing on the wall,
Pink feels like a silky pink dress,
Pink looks like a pair of earrings we can put in our ears,
Pink makes me feel joyful and happy,
Pink is my favourite colour.

Tara Smith (8)
St Ninian's Primary School, Gourock

Pink

Pink is Miriam's big bright pencil case,
Pink is my mum's beautiful roses growing in the garden,
Pink is my lungs breathing very fast,
Pink tastes like strawberry jam tingling in my mouth,
Pink smells like lovely smooth strawberry ice cream,
Pink sounds like paint splashing on the tall wall,
Pink feels like my brother's frilly knickers,
Pink looks like the lovely hair band,
Pink makes me happy and joyful inside,
Pink is my favourite colour.

Niamh Salmon (8)
St Ninian's Primary School, Gourock

Pink

Pink is beautiful,
Pink is wonderful,
Pink is bright,
Pink tastes like lovely strawberry ice cream,
Pink smells like a lovely pink rose,
Pink sounds like a car driving past,
Pink feels like frilly pink underwear,
Pink looks like a bright pink flower,
Pink makes me happy,
Pink is my favourite colour.

Jennifer Askew (8)
St Ninian's Primary School, Gourock

Red

Red is like blood,
Red is like a ruby,
Red is like the heart in my body,
Red tastes like red wine in my mouth,
Red smells like a fresh cherry in my house,
Red sounds like loud heartbeats,
Red feels like red ink in a tub,
Red looks like veins in my arm,
Red makes me think of blood,
Red is my favourite colour.

Liam James McEwen (8)
St Ninian's Primary School, Gourock

White

White is the fluffy clouds in the sky,
White is bumpy, long bones in your body,
White is like the soft, fluffy sheep in the farm,
White tastes like the hard sugar which melts in your mouth,
White smells like the smoke which comes out of a chimney,
White sounds like the heavy rain hitting the ground,
White feels like messy paint on your hands,
White looks like the cold, fluffy snow,
White makes me jump and very happy,
White is my favourite colour.

Miriam Graham (8)
St Ninian's Primary School, Gourock

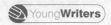

Snow

Ice-cold snowflakes falling softly,
The scenery looks so pretty and lovely.

I can't wait to go out and play,
All I know is it's going to be a cold day.

The snow is glistening on the ground,
People are sledging all around.

Lots of children are having fun,
Please don't come back, nice hot sun.

Kirsty–Ann McCluskey (11)
St Ninian's Primary School, Gourock

White

White is a fluffy cloud in the sky,
White is a woolly sheep in the field,
White is a long piece of chalk,
White tastes like sugar going in a cup of tea,
White smells the smoke coming out a tall chimney,
White sounds like a beautiful swan at a pond,
White feels like my bumpy bones in my body,
White looks like fluffy snow falling to the ground,
White makes me feel like it's a winter morning.

Amy O'Neill (8)
St Ninian's Primary School, Gourock

Winter

Winter ice skated
Along a frozen lake,
Wearing a purple and white scarf,
Wrapped tightly round his neck,
He had woollen, gloved hands,
Interlocked behind his back.
He slowly slid along,
Hopping from one foot to the other
And every time he passed a tree the next lot of birds
Would start to sing.
People smiled,
As he glided past their little cottages,
Children opened their bedroom window
To wave to him
And slowly
The green trees turned to white
Behind his ice trail,
A little wren sat on the fluffy bobble of his purple
Christmassy hat,
He smiled and chuckled,
A small chuckle,
As he continued to skate
Down his frozen friend.

Ruairidh Sherrington (11)
Scoraig 5-14 School, Garve

Great White Shark

Come swim with the shark, come swim!
Down to the depths of the ocean.
Meet the Great White Shark,
The king of the sea,
Swimming through the waves,
As fast as a bullet.
It keeps on going, on and on,
It never stops.
It crunches on meat and bone,
Until it's dead,
Its sharp teeth and scary eyes,
As it swims along the big, wide ocean,
His large mouth open,
With his gills breathing water,
Eating anything,
It can never get full.
A very thick skin:
A thousand knives wouldn't get through it,
Always kills,
Always swims,
Always eats,
Will never stop.

Murdo Brudenell (10)
Scoraig 5-14 School, Garve

The Tree Incident

In the trees, birds chattering,
Tree houses thoughts of fun and joy,
The sweet smells of the autumn leaves and bark,
Crispy, refreshing air on the tip of my nose,
Disturbed by noise down on the ground,
Ruins my thoughts,
'You know that was our family tree!'
Clenching white fists, bright red sky.
Heat waves.
Next, name calling, rising temper,
Both standing,
Thud!
Blood on the ground from my face,
The opponent in regret and grief.

Ise Forsyth (11)
Scoraig 5-14 School, Garve

Coracle

Fun, unstable,
Floating, sinking, learning,
Sky above me, sea below me,
Paddling, singing, racing,
Willow canvas,
Engine.

Elijah Weightman (11)
Scoraig 5-14 School, Garve

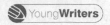

My Cat

Noise-maker
Loud-purrer
Love-seeker
Friend-finder
Mouse-hunter
Bird-stalker
Tree-climber
Fast-runner
Game-player
Dog-chaser.

A fantastic pet.

Jamie Cutler (12)
Scoraig 5-14 School, Garve

Space

S tars shine in the night,
P lanets are big and round,
A stronauts fly up to space,
C omets go faster than everything,
E arth is the best planet.

Peter Hannon (7)
Slamannan Primary School, Falkirk

Space

S tars that fill the solar system,
P lanets that are round and might have life,
A liens that live on other worlds,
C omets that shoot across the sky,
E arth, the planet that has life.

Hannah Gill (8)
Slamannan Primary School, Falkirk

Young Writers Information

We hope you have enjoyed reading this book - and that you will continue to enjoy it in the coming years.

If you like reading and writing poetry drop us a line, or give us a call, and we'll send you a free information pack.

Alternatively if you would like to order further copies of this book or any of our other titles, then please give us a call or log onto our website at www.youngwriters.co.uk

Young Writers Information
Remus House
Coltsfoot Drive
Peterborough
PE2 9JX
(01733) 890066